THE SUPERCHARGED GREEN JUICE & SMOOTHIE DIET

THE SUPERCHARGED GREEN JUICE & SMOOTHIE DIET

Over 100 recipes to boost weight loss, detoxification and energy using green vegetables and super-supplements

Thanks to my wonderful boys, Nathan, Isaac and Simeon, and to my husband, Chris, for their ongoing support and for taste-testing all my recipes.

The Supercharged Green Juice & Smoothie Diet
Christine Bailey

First published in the United Kingdom and Ireland
in 2016 by Nourish, an imprint of
Watkins Media Limited
19 Cecil Court
London WC2N 4EZ

enquiries@nourishbooks.com

Publisher: Grace Cheetham
Editor: Jan Cutler
Managing Designer: Georgina Hewitt
Designer: Sally Williams
Commissioned Photography: Toby Scott
Food Stylist: Sara Lewis
Prop Stylist: Linda Berlin
Production: Uzma Taj

A CIP record for this book is available from the British Library

ISBN: 978-1-84899-292-4

10 9 8 7 6 5 4 3 2 1

Typeset in Rockwell
Colour reproduction by XY Digital
Printed in China

Publisher's Note
While every care has been taken in compiling the recipes for this book, Watkins Media Limited, or any other persons who have been involved in working on this publication, cannot accept responsibility for any errors or omissions, inadvertent or not, that may be found in the recipes or text, nor for any problems that may arise as a result of preparing one of these recipes. If you are pregnant or breastfeeding or have any special dietary requirements or medical conditions, it is advisable to consult a medical professional before following any of the recipes contained in this book.

Notes on the Recipes
All recipes serve 1
Unless otherwise stated:
- Use medium fruit and vegetables
- Fruit and vegetables are washed and unpeeled
- Use fresh ingredients, including herbs and spices
- Use organic ingredients where possible
- Do not mix metric and imperial measurements
- 1 tsp = 5ml   1 tbsp = 15ml   1 cup = 250ml

The nutrition symbols refer to the recipes only, not including ingredient alternatives, optional ingredients or serving suggestions. Protein powders are considered to be vegan and soya-free (pea, rice or hemp). Peanuts have been classed as nuts.

nourishbooks.com

Key to Symbols

- G Gluten-free
- D Dairy-free
- S Soya-free
- N Nut-free
- SE Seed-free
- CI Citrus-free
- V Suitable for vegans

Feel Great, Look Great – the Supercharged Way

Supercharged green juices and smoothies offer you a completely natural programme for achieving a healthy weight while improving your health and vitality. Whether you need to lose just a few pounds or are looking for a more significant weight loss in the long term, the supercharged drinks in this book will help you to achieve your goal. These nutritious green drinks will also flood your body with vitamins, minerals and phytonutrients to keep you feeling vibrant and energized as you shift those excess pounds.

In the chapters that follow, you will find your ideal weight-loss plan: (1) a fast-track three-day juice-only detox to blast that excess weight while it cleanses and refreshes your body; (2) a week-long juice and smoothie programme for effective weight loss and rejuvenation – this plan is higher in protein and fibre to ensure you maintain energy as you lose pounds, and it can either follow the three-day detox or be used as a stand-alone diet; (3) a 30-day juice and smoothie plan for longer-term weight loss and as a health boost; or (4) a permanent way to incorporate longevity-boosting juices and smoothies into your diet to help you maintain a healthy weight for good and to give you vitality. There are over 100 recipes to supercharge your health and to nourish and revitalize your body.

The power of green foods

Although we are all aware of the importance of vegetables in our diet, very few of us eat the optimum amount. In fact, our modern diet steers most of us in the opposite direction – and it is making us fat and ill. There is a predominance of processed, calorie-dense but nutrient-poor foods in the typical Western diet, and it is contributing to an alarming rise in obesity, diabetes and other health conditions. Devoid of essential nutrients, the typical diet today leaves our bodies lacking vitality and craving nourishment by prompting us to eat more and ultimately to gain weight.

In spite of this mistreatment, our bodies have the power to renew and heal when supplied with nutrient-dense vegetables plus supercharged ingredients – highly potent nutrients taken in very small doses – combined in the drinks in this book. These supercharged ingredients can propel your weight loss by supporting body systems such as detoxification, adrenal and thyroid health, metabolism and blood sugar balance – all of which play a significant role in achieving a healthy weight.

What is a 'green' drink?

A green juice is one that is focused on nutrient-dense green vegetables, particularly leafy greens and herbs, with a small amount of low-sugar fruits such as citrus fruits or green apples. A green smoothie is similar, although the vegetables and fruits are blended with water, nut milk, herbal tea or a fermented drink.

The drinks will fill you up quickly and support your body's natural ability to cleanse and detox – helping you to lose weight. The juices and smoothies are equally nutrient dense but the smoothies also contain protein and fibre, which keeps you feeling fuller for longer, balances your blood sugar and makes it easier for you to lose weight. They make an excellent start to the day.

Less equals more

There are many reasons why you might consider incorporating green juices and smoothies into your daily diet for weight loss. Many people have compromised digestion – whether that's due to poor diet, stress or lifestyle habits – but juicing 'pre-digests' the nutrients, allowing you to absorb and utilize them efficiently. This provides your body with the nutrients it craves and it will stimulate your weight loss. The weight-loss plans in this book help you to break the cycle of unhealthy eating habits, they allow your digestive system to reset and repair, and they enhance cleansing, which all contribute to weight loss.

A boost from supercharged ingredients

Most juice cleanses lack the health benefits of protein and health-promoting supercharged foods. These extras are derived from specific plants, sea algae, bee products, natural oils and extra-potent berries that can be taken in very small doses because the power they contain is so great (see The Supercharged Storecupboard starting on page 11). Each drink in this book contains at least one supercharged food, so each is super-powered above and beyond its fruit and vegetable components. My weight-loss recipes taste good and work synergistically to nourish and enhance your body while helping you to achieve a healthy and attractive weight.

Supercharged weight loss and wellness

Anyone can benefit from the nourishment and feelings of renewed health when taking my supercharged green juices and smoothies, but the plans are specifically designed for losing weight. They can be an effective way to break unhealthy eating habits, kick-start your metabolism and promote fat burning. As well as losing weight, your skin will become more radiant and your energy levels will soar.

Why balance is important

Commonly followed juice and smoothie recipes focus on fruit, but these drinks can have a damaging effect on blood sugar levels because of the concentrated sweetness of the fruit. Blood sugar imbalances lead to energy slumps, irritability and cravings, and will affect your ability to lose weight. My green drinks, by contrast, emphasize vegetables, and particularly leafy green vegetables and herbs – a little fruit is added to give the juice flavour.

Vegetable *juices* are low in protein, so for the three-day plan I have included a scoop of protein powder to be added to one or two of the daily juices. This will support blood sugar balance and muscle mass. The other plans include *smoothies*, many of which have added protein.

How to use this book

The juices and smoothies in this book are divided into programmes. These include a three-day juice detox, a seven-day plan and a 30-day plan. Details of each plan are on the following pages. There is also a section called Your Supercharged Green for Life, which includes a range of delicious combinations to enjoy at any time to maintain a healthy weight and feel fabulous.

The drinks contain nutrients to deliver particular health benefits. On pages 150–157 you will find a star rating for each drink under the following benefits: weight loss, cleansing, radiance, energy, immune boost, and brain and stress health. Choose the drink that has the highest star rating for the benefit you are seeking.

The Supercharged Diet Basics

Read this section before you turn to the diet chapters, so that you can prepare yourself for your diet plan. Getting your body ready for the diets begins the week before, so plan ahead to get the best results from the programme you choose to follow. You will also find advice on how to proceed after your diet programme has finished so that the benefits of the diet will not be lost once you return to your usual routine.

What equipment will you need?

For juicing, I recommend you invest in a masticating juicer, as this will enable you to extract the greatest amount of nutrients from your ingredients. The cheaper centrifugal juicers are not as efficient in juicing leafy greens or herbs, which are the focus of the recipes in this book.

To make the smoothies, you can use a Nutribullet or a high-speed/high-quality blender. As all the recipes serve one, they are ideal for the Nutribullet – just remember to fill the bullet with the correct amount of liquid (up to the line) before blending. Nutribullets are also capable of blending or crushing ice, nuts and seeds, which are included in some of the recipes. I developed all the recipes using both a high-speed blender and a Nutribullet, and both are equally effective.

The only other pieces of equipment you will need are chopping boards, a sharp knife, measuring spoons and ice-cube trays so that you can create chilled and slushy smoothies.

How to choose your programme

There are a number of specially designed programmes for you to follow. You can select whichever plan is appropriate for your weight-loss goals. Once you have completed one plan you can move on to another or adopt the guidelines suggested in Chapter 4, Your Supercharged Green for Life. All the programmes will encourage weight loss and will promote clearer, healthier-looking skin, ease digestion, cleanse and recharge the body, and promote detoxification. If you are simply looking to maintain a healthy weight, you can select any juice or smoothie in the book to suit your taste or health requirements.

The programmes are suitable for most people, but they are not suitable if you are under 18, pregnant or breastfeeding. If you have an ongoing medical condition or are on long-term medication, please discuss with your doctor or healthcare practitioner before starting this, or any other, diet plan. These juice programmes should not replace long-term healthy-eating and lifestyle changes but are designed to kick-start healthy, effective weight loss.

Your Supercharged Three-Day Detox

This *juice-only* plan is an easy way to kick-start a healthier-eating programme to help you lose weight. It will also cleanse and revitalize your energy levels, and it is perfect for preparing your body for a special occasion or as a yearly or quarterly cleansing programme to recharge your body. You will find full details on pages 24–27.

Your Supercharged Diet Week

If you can commit to seven days of *juicing and smoothies*, this plan is for you. You'll experience notable weight loss while feeling energized and refreshed. Choose this plan if you have more than a few pounds to lose and you can commit to a week of green drinks, or if you would like a more intense cleansing programme. You will find more details on pages 46–49.

Your Supercharged Diet Month

This 30-day *juice and smoothie* programme is perfect for anyone who is aiming to make significant longer-term changes to their weight and health. This plan requires more commitment than the shorter plans. It combines supercharged drinks with a light meal each day and it includes smoothies with protein to support healthy muscle mass and blood sugar balance. Choose this plan if you have more than half a stone (3.2kg/7lb) to lose and you want to commit to a longer-term follow-on programme or if you are looking for a more intense cleansing programme. You will find more details on pages 74–77.

Your Supercharged Green for Life

You may be looking for an effective and easy way to power up your health in the long term and maintain a healthy weight. If so, try to include one or two of the juices or smoothies from this chapter – or from the other chapters in the book – in your daily eating regime. Take a drink for breakfast, as an accompaniment to a meal or as an energizing snack. You will find more details on pages 116–117.

How to get started

Read through the explanations of the diet plans in the chapters that follow, and decide which plan you would like to use. To get the most benefit, aim for a week's diet clean-up first as explained in each diet's programme details. Whichever plan you decide to follow, read the instructions in each chapter regarding the quantities and kinds of liquids to drink each day.

See if you can find a 'juice buddy' for support and to help you stay scheduled and busy, particularly around meal times.

In the following storecupboard section, you will find a list of all the supercharged ingredients in the book. Use this alongside your diet plan to decide which supercharged ingredients to add to your drinks. As explained on page 18, you do not need to use all of the supercharged ingredients that are featured in the diet you intend to follow, so you may want to aim for the kinds of ingredients that offer the best benefits for you personally (see The Quick Look starting on page 150). You will find plenty of information in the pages that follow to guide you.

Plan your shop

If you are following the three-day detox you will want to buy all the foods you need in advance, but for the seven-day diet and the 30-day diet you will need to shop more regularly to be sure your fruit and vegetables are really fresh. Look at the diet plans and decide on the drinks you want to have so that you can get organized.

Buy organic produce, if possible, to maximize the nutrients in the drinks and to reduce your exposure to harmful chemicals. Organic, grass-fed meat and wild game are also often richer in healthy omega-3 fats and CLA (conjugated linoleic acid) and lower in saturated fats.

Wash all your vegetables and fruits before using. If you're short of time in the morning, you can wash your ingredients the night before and put them in the fridge.

Storing juices and smoothies

Juices and smoothies are perishable and ideally should be consumed immediately after making them; however, you can store juices for up to 24 hours without too much loss of nutrients. This is helpful if you are taking your drinks to work or if you want to make up a batch in the morning for the rest of the day. The best way to store your drinks is to put them in a glass jar (BPA-free plastic works too) with an airtight lid and fill it to the very top. This reduces oxidation and the loss of nutrients. Store it in the fridge and consume it within 24 hours.

Remember that it is important to clean your juicer and blender properly each time to prevent any food remnants from contaminating them with mould growth.

Potential side effects

Occasionally, people experience side effects when following a juice programme. The majority of these will be temporary and should be resolved either during the programme or when you resume a healthy diet. If any symptoms continue or become severe, it is important to consult your healthcare practitioner for advice. Common symptoms can include hunger, fatigue, headaches, dizziness, changes in bowel movements and irritability.

It is important to ensure that you are drinking sufficient amounts throughout the day, so you may need to check you are drinking enough water, coconut water or herbal teas in addition to the juices. If you are struggling with your blood sugar levels, add a nut milk (page 19) or a handful of nuts, or take one of the protein-based smoothies. Take these before bedtime if you find that your sleep is disturbed.

Continue to benefit from your diet plan

Not only is it wise to prepare for your diet, but it is also important to plan for the transition afterwards. This is essential if you want to reap maximum benefits. Don't spend time and energy cleansing your body only to put rubbish back in as soon as you have finished. When planning your post-detox diet, focus on including plenty of raw and lightly cooked vegetables with lean proteins, and keep processed foods out. Watch your intake of caffeine, sweeteners and sugars too – focus on whole foods, organically grown, if possible, to keep your food free of chemicals.

The diet should make you feel clean and fresh, so maximize the benefits by making lasting changes to your diet. To keep the weight off, pay attention to how many carbohydrates you consume. Ideally, each meal should focus on lean, quality protein (about one-quarter of your plate, or about 120–150g/4¼–5½oz) with a colourful selection of vegetables (to fill half your plate) including leafy green vegetables.

Rather than worrying too much about weighing every food item, I suggest you focus on how you fill your plate.

Half your plate should be low-starch vegetables, including broccoli, dark-green leaves, cauliflower, Brussels sprouts, courgettes, fennel, cucumber, tomatoes, green beans, olives, lettuce, onions, leeks, aubergine, peppers and mushrooms. A quarter of your plate should contain protein-rich foods, such as fish, seafood, lean meat, eggs, nuts, low-fat dairy (if you can tolerate it), tofu or tempeh (or other beans or lentils, if you are vegan). A portion will weigh roughly as explained above. On the remaining quarter, add one portion of cooked starchy vegetables, such as squash, or whole grains.

The Supercharged Storecupboard

Supercharged foods are natural ingredients that not only provide a wealth of nutrients in a concentrated form but also have the ability to restore balance in the body. There is no such thing as a perfect food, so the emphasis in this book is to promote a wide variety of nutrient-dense natural foods that can work synergistically to promote health and support body systems to accompany a weight-loss programme.

The foods listed in this section are a selection of superstar ingredients that have been chosen for their ability to assist fat-burning, build muscle and stabilize blood sugar levels while promoting health and longevity. Many of the ingredients are known to boost liver function, cleansing and detoxification, which are particularly effective in promoting weight loss. They have all been included in the recipes throughout the book. Many of the supercharged foods are now available in local health shops and supermarkets; all can be purchased online.

Algae

These include chlorella, spirulina and seaweed flakes. Both spirulina and chlorella are excellent sources of digestible protein, making them valuable for vegans. As they are strongly cleansing, I recommend that you introduce them gradually into your diet to allow the body to adapt to their properties.

Chlorella Known for its detoxification and energizing properties, chlorella is a single-celled, water-grown alga. It is rich in chlorophyll, a nutrient that can support energy as well as detoxification in the body. Chlorella is extremely rich in vitamins, minerals, amino acids, essential fatty acids, polysaccharides and other beneficial compounds. Buy as a powder for use in recipes or blend up 'cracked cell' tablets. Cracked cell ensures the nutrients are readily digestible.

Nori is an edible red seaweed that is eaten in East Asia, especially Japan. It provides protein and omega-3 fats and is a useful source of iron and calcium. It also contains iodine and trace minerals, which are needed to support thyroid function and metabolism. Buy as flakes.

Spirulina belongs to a class of single-celled, blue-green spiral algae. It is rich in chlorophyll, protein, vitamins, minerals, essential fatty acids, nucleic acids (RNA and DNA), polysaccharides and a vast spectrum of antioxidants. Buy as a powder or tablets.

Bee products

There are a number of good-quality bee products that have powerful anti-ageing and health-promoting benefits.

Bee pollen is incredibly nutrient dense, supplied with amino acids, vitamins and minerals. A great source of energizing B vitamins, enzymes, amino acids and polysaccharides, it is thought to regenerate the body at a cellular level. Buy as granules.

Honey is a traditional sweetener. Raw, unprocessed honey and manuka honey are rich in enzymes that can assist digestion. They are powerful immune boosters with anti-microbial properties and are rich in antioxidants. Honey is, nevertheless, a sugar, so it should be used only in very small amounts.

Royal jelly is the food given to bee larvae by the nurse bee for the first days of their life. It is thought to rejuvenate and regenerate the body and is often considered to be an anti-ageing food. Particularly rich in folate as well as other B vitamins, it is valuable as a brain and energy tonic and is also nourishing for the adrenal glands. Buy as a powder or in capsules.

Berries and fruit

The fruits listed here are just a few of those known for their diverse range of antioxidants and vitamin C. Fresh and dried berries add a sweetness to blends and are perfect for boosting energy. You can buy blended superberry powders that can be useful in the recipes. Certain specific berries are also available and beneficial for their concentration of valuable nutrients.

Acai berry The dark-purple acai is an exceptionally high-antioxidant fruit and a very concentrated source of anthocyanins, which are known for their protective, anti-ageing benefits. The health properties of acai are boosted by the presence of healthy fats, fibre, phytosterols (plant fats that help to lower LDL cholesterol) and amino acids. They are also naturally low in sugars. Buy as a powder, freeze-dried capsules or as the unsweetened frozen pulp.

Amla Also known as Indian gooseberry, amla is exceptionally high in vitamin C, making it a protective, immune-supporting fruit. It contains chromium, which the body needs for blood sugar balance, and gut-friendly fibre. Buy as a powder.

Baobab fruit has a unique, tangy taste like a blend of grapefruit, pear and vanilla. With three times the vitamin C of an orange, iron and the minerals calcium, potassium and magnesium, baobab is energizing and alkalizing. It is also rich in fibre and is fabulous for digestive health. Buy as a powder.

Blueberry Freeze-dried blueberry powder is a concentrated source of nutrients. Packed with phytochemicals, including anthocyanins, and with vitamin C, vitamin E and carotenoids, blueberries help support immune function, cognitive health, and protect against cancer and urinary tract infections. Buy as a powder.

Camu camu The small, reddish, cherry-like camu camu fruit is exceptionally high in vitamin C. Studies show that it contains a concentration of vitamin C of between 2 and 3 per cent (approximately 3,000mg per 100g/3½oz of pulp), which is one of the highest known of any fruit. It also contains a range of antioxidants, B vitamins and minerals, such as potassium, iron and calcium. It is high in fibre and particularly useful for aiding weight loss and detoxification. Buy as a freeze-dried powder and use in small amounts only, due to its exceptionally high vitamin-C content. Between ¼ and ½ teaspoon daily is sufficient – an excess may have a laxative effect. Do not heat camu camu, as this will destroy the vitamin C.

Elderberry is known for its anti-viral and immune-supporting properties. It is rich in flavonoids and exceptionally rich in vitamin C. It also contains beta-carotene, potassium, fibre and vitamin B6. It is traditionally used to relieve respiratory infections, arthritis and to combat an upset stomach. Buy as a syrup or tincture.

Goji berry (also known as wolfberry) is frequently used in Chinese medicine for boosting longevity and enhancing energy and immune health. It is high in amino acids and rich in carotenoids, vitamin C, various B vitamins and iron. Buy as the dried berries and as a powder.

Incan berry (also known as goldenberry, Cape gooseberry and Chinese lantern). The dried berries are delicious as a snack and have a citrus, slightly sweet–sour flavour. Packed with antioxidants, vitamins A and C, they are useful for strengthening the immune system. Buy as the sun-dried berries.

Lucuma The delicious Peruvian lucuma fruit is useful as a natural sweetener and has a caramel-like flavour. It contains a variety of nutrients including vitamins, minerals and fibre, such as beta-carotene, vitamins B1, B2, B3, B5 and niacin, as well as the minerals iron, potassium, calcium and phosphorus. Buy as a powder.

Maqui berry This traditional Chilean food is renowned for its anti-ageing properties. It is one of the highest antioxidant fruits in the world and is especially rich in polyphenols and anthocyanins, which help to protect and repair the body's cells. It's a great source of vitamin C. Buy as a powder or as capsules.

Montmorency cherry This tart cherry delivers a much greater content of anthocyanins than sweet cherries, as well as higher amounts of other nutrients. It has been shown to improve insulin function, aid weight loss and support cognitive function. Tart cherries are a natural source of melatonin to promote sleep. They are anti-inflammatory and may help lower your risk of gout and reduce the pain and inflammation associated with osteoarthritis. Available as a concentrated juice or dried sour cherries.

Mulberry leaf has long been used for the prevention and treatment of diabetes, as it contains compounds that suppress high blood sugar levels. Mulberry leaves are high in antioxidants including quercetin, known for its anti-inflammatory properties. Buy as a powder.

Noni is the common name for *Morinda citrifolia*, a tropical tree native to the Polynesian islands. The ripe fruit has a citrus-like flavour and is rich in polysaccharide compounds known to support immune health. Packed with powerful antioxidants, noni is a wonderful anti-ageing fruit. Buy as a powder.

Pomegranate has high levels of antioxidants and potassium, which can help maintain healthy blood pressure. It also contains phytoestrogenic compounds, making it helpful for balancing the female hormones. Buy as the fresh fruit or as a powder.

Sea buckthorn This orange berry is known for its skin-regenerating properties. It is very high in vitamin C and quercetin, an anti-inflammatory phytonutrient. It contains omega-7 fat, making it very nourishing for the skin. Buy as 100 per cent pure sea buckthorn juice.

Cacao

This is the raw, unprocessed source of chocolate. Raw, unsweetened cacao powder, which is high in antioxidant flavonols, is very different from the common, commercial cocoa drinks and chocolates. Cacao is derived from cacao beans, one of nature's most supercharged foods due to its mineral content and wide array of unique and varied properties. Raw cacao is one of the best food sources of magnesium. It is also exceptionally rich in chromium, which is used to help control blood sugar. It contains a number of compounds known to boost mood and relaxation such as tryptophan, theobromine and phenylethylamine (PEA). As well as the powder and butter, some recipes use cacao nibs, which are slightly bitter and have a strong chocolate flavour and a wonderful crunchy texture.

Dried fungi, grasses, herbs, leaves, roots and vegetables

Aloe vera is particularly useful in supporting digestive health and blood sugar balance, and is an ideal cleansing tonic, great for radiant skin. Buy as a juice or gel. Look for brands that contain 100 per cent aloe.

Ashwagandha – often referred to as 'Indian ginseng' – is an adaptogenic herb (to enhance endurance) widely used in many parts of Asia. It is also used as a rejuvenating tonic, sedative and immune-supporting food, and is valued as an anti-ageing herb. It may help to calm the mind, improve memory and harmonize body systems. Buy as a powder or tea.

Astragalus is one of the great tonic herbs used to support the immune system and strengthen the body. It is a popular energy tonic for athletes and anyone looking for more day-to-day energy and vitality. Buy as a powder.

Chaga is one of the most popular medicinal mushrooms and is known for its strong immune-enhancing properties, its high levels of antioxidants and its anti-viral properties. It is an amazing health-and-longevity tonic, full of phytonutrients that slow down the ageing process. Chaga contains a range of active ingredients: sterols, triterpenes, saponins and polysaccharides and it is also immuno-stimulatory. Buy as a powder.

Cissus quadrangularis is a perennial plant and a member of the grape family. It is used to help stress levels, lower high cortisol and reduce anxiety. It is also taken to maintain healthy bones, digestive function and respiratory health. Buy as a powder.

Ginkgo biloba is one of the oldest trees known for its beneficial properties and has been used to support health for thousands of years. The leaf extracts contain several active constituents with neuroprotective and cardioprotective properties. Rich in flavonoids, which help to strengthen the capillaries, promote healthy blood flow to the brain and maintain cognitive health, ginkgo is ideal for a mental boost. Buy as a powder or tincture.

Ginseng products are usually used as a general tonic and adaptogen to help the body adapt to daily stress. They are particularly useful for improving physical and mental performance, vitality and to reduce fatigue. Ginseng contains a range of compounds: ginsenosides, saponins, phytosterols, peptides, polysaccharides, fatty acids and polyacetylenes, as well as vitamins and minerals. There are several species of ginseng: *Panax ginseng*, often chosen for its abilities to help tackle stress; American ginseng, *Panax quinquefolius,* to improve blood sugar or to ease dry coughs; Siberian ginseng, *Eleutherococcus senticosus*, an excellent energy, stress and blood tonic – great for athletes. Buy ginseng products as a powder or tincture.

Green coffee is unroasted coffee beans that are particularly rich in phytochemicals known as chlorogenic acid. These have been shown to improve insulin function, boost metabolism and weight loss. Buy as a powder or capsules. Do not take if you are sensitive to caffeine.

Green tea and matcha green tea powder Of green and black tea, green is the least processed and provides the most antioxidant polyphenols, notably a catechin called epigallocatechin-3-gallate (EGCG), which is believed to be responsible for most of the tea's health benefits. For optimal benefits, use matcha green tea powder, because when you drink matcha you ingest the whole leaf, not just the brewed water. One glass of matcha is the equivalent of 10 glasses of green tea in terms of its nutritional value and antioxidant content. It is an effective fat burner and energizing food, and its high antioxidant levels mean it is also helpful in protecting the body from harmful free-radical damage. Green tea also contains the amino acid L-theanine, which stimulates the production of alpha brain waves to create a state of calmness and mental alertness. Buy as a powder or use an infusion of green tea in drinks.

Gynostemma This adaptogenic herb is taken to invigorate the body and restore strength and vitality as well as to calm the body to relieve anxiety. The main active ingredients are saponins, which have potent antioxidant, liver-supportive and anti-inflammatory activity. Buy as tea bags or as a powder.

Maca A radish-like root, maca is known for its adaptogenic properties and has the ability to help the body adjust to stress, build up resistance to disease and support immunity. It can also be taken as an energy food for combating fatigue. Its delicious, sweet butterscotch flavour means that it blends beautifully with cacao in drinks. Maca works directly on the hypothalamus and pituitary glands: the body's 'master glands', which help to regulate other glands, such as the levels of sex hormones in men and women. Buy as a powder.

Milk thistle is a great addition to cleansing programmes, because it is packed with antioxidants, which help to protect the body from damage. Buy as a tea, powder and tincture.

Moringa leaf Although various parts of the *Moringa oleifera* plant can be used, it is the leaves that are most widely available in powdered form. They are highly nutritious and particularly rich in beta-carotene, vitamin C, protein, calcium, iron and potassium. They are also rich in chlorophyll, making them alkalizing, cleansing and energizing. Buy as a powder.

Mucuna pruriens (also known as velvet bean and cowitch) is mostly known for containing a substance called L-dopa from which a very powerful neurotransmitter (a chemical at a nerve ending) is formed. L-dopa is an amino acid that converts into the 'focus and motivation' neurotransmitter, dopamine, making it effective for boosting mood. Mucuna can also help increase the production of human growth hormone, thereby boosting lean muscle and breaking down fat. Buy as a powder or capsules.

Turmeric root The health benefits in this curry spice lie in the active ingredient, curcumin. Studies have shown that turmeric possesses a wealth of properties including anti-inflammatory and antioxidant benefits. It has also been shown to help support brain function and is valued for its anti-ageing benefits. Buy as the root or ground.

Wheatgrass powder is well known for its rejuvenating and alkalizing properties. Light and clean tasting, wheatgrass is packed with chlorophyll, making it incredibly energizing. It is also rich in B vitamins, antioxidants and vitamin A, as well as numerous minerals, including manganese, zinc and magnesium. Its high fibre content means it is also a great addition to green juices and is beneficial for digestive health. Buy as a powder. There are also green superfood blend powders that will include wheatgrass and other green supercharged foods.

Yacon is a tuber native to South America. It is rich in inulin, a type of fibre that breaks down slowly and provides food for the beneficial bacteria in the gut. Yacon is enjoyed as a natural sweetener because it has a low glycaemic index, meaning that it can be helpful for balancing blood sugar levels. It has a light molasses flavour. Buy as a syrup.

Fats and oils

Natural fat is an essential macronutrient for health and longevity. The right types of fats in the correct proportions are important for brain function, lowering inflammation, providing sustained energy, and for maintaining healthy cell membranes and nervous system function. They form the building blocks of hormones, which influence many biological processes throughout the body. In addition, fat helps to keep you feeling fuller for longer, it reduces cravings and helps you achieve a healthy weight loss. Certain fats have also been shown to boost the metabolism – so eating fat can actually assist weight loss. The following natural fats are used in the recipes in addition to the fats found in other foods, such as nuts and seeds.

Coconut oil provides richness to smoothies. Although it contains saturated fats, it is predominately rich in medium-chain triglycerides, which sustain energy levels and increase the metabolic rate. This makes it ideal for taking before workouts, for example. It also provides lauric acid and caprylic acid, which support immune health and possess anti-microbial properties. For quality, buy organic virgin coconut oil, available in jars.

Lecithin granules Made from soya or sunflower seeds, lecithin contains a naturally occurring mixture of phospholipids. Phospholipids are an essential component of cell membranes and particularly important for brain health and the nervous system. Buy as granules.

MCT oil MCT stands for medium-chain triglycerides. It is comprised primarily of caprylic and capric fatty acids, and is a light-yellow, odourless, translucent liquid at room temperature. It is normally derived from coconut oil. MCT oil is processed by the liver and immediately burned to produce energy. It may increase metabolism, thereby helping you to burn fat. Buy in bottles.

Omega-3 and -6 oils There is a range of omega-rich oils that provide a good balance of the essential fatty acids omega-3 and -6. These include flaxseed oil, chia oil and hempseed oil, as well as omega-blended oils. Store these oils in the fridge. Buy as organic cold-pressed oils.

Fermented drinks

Kefir and kombucha are fermented drinks that have been used for thousands of years to promote health and vitality. They provide a wide variety of beneficial probiotic bacteria, which are essential for supporting overall health, immune function, digestion and detoxification. Some of the recipes include kombucha, water kefir, milk kefir or coconut kefir to boost your intake of these beneficial bacteria. You can either make your own fermented drinks (see page 20) or purchase them from health shops or online.

Nuts and seeds

Many of the recipes include nuts and seeds to provide additional protein – essential for maintaining muscle mass – healthy fats, vitamins and minerals. Super-seeds are:

Chia seed is a rich source of protein, omega-3 fats and soluble fibre to balance blood sugar and support bowel health. It also contains valuable minerals including calcium and iron. Its high soluble-fibre content makes it absorb water very easily, making it plump up when added to liquids. Once digested, chia expands in the stomach, creating a sensation of fullness. Buy the whole seed for use in the recipes.

Flaxseed Like chia, flaxseed is known for its fibre content and high levels of omega-3 fats. It also contains lignans, a type of phytochemical (plant chemical) that can help to balance hormone levels. A good source of protein, flaxseed is also useful for stabilizing blood sugar levels and supporting energy. Buy the ground flaxseed.

Hemp seed Hemp provides a wealth of nutrition, including good levels of essential omega-3 fatty acids, amino acids and fibre. It is also a rich source of minerals, especially iron, potassium, zinc and magnesium. Hemp protein powder gives smoothies a rich, earthy flavour. The seeds add a lovely nutty flavour to drinks. Buy as soft, raw shelled hemp seeds.

Protein powders

In order to support a healthy weight loss and retain muscle, it is important to consume sufficient protein. For this reason I have added protein powders to some of the recipes. These can be particularly helpful in stabilizing blood sugar levels and keeping you feeling fuller for longer as well as maintaining muscle mass, which is important for boosting metabolism.

If you are active or work out regularly, including protein powders post-training can assist your recovery. Protein powders vary tremendously in terms of their constituents, so choose a high-quality powder without unnecessary fillers, additives and sweeteners. You will find a range of flavours, but I use plain, vanilla or chocolate in this book. Whey protein powders are popular and contain a good bioavailable source of amino acids and other components to support health; however, some people find dairy products difficult to digest. The recipes in this book use soya- and dairy-free vegan protein powders such as pea protein, hemp, rice or a sprouted superfood blend, which are also low in allergens and highly nutritious.

Supplements and minerals

Collagen is a natural protein component of the skin and the main building block for cells, tissues and organs. About one-third of the protein content in your body is made up of collagen, which is found in the bones, muscles and tissues of the organs. Collagen, keratin and elastin give the skin its strength, elasticity and structure. Taking a collagen supplement can be helpful for improving skin health, supporting the gut lining, the bones, joints and healthy muscle mass. It is normally derived from marine or bovine sources. Buy as a powder.

Colostrum is the first milk produced by breastfeeding mothers, and it is renowned for its immune-boosting properties. Bovine colostrum is used as a supplement and has a similar structure to colostrum produced by humans. Research has supported its many health benefits, particularly for improving digestive function and nutrient absorption, but also for balancing the immune system, increasing energy and reducing inflammation. Buy as a powder or as capsules.

Glutamine is the most common amino acid found in the muscles and this makes it a popular supplement to use post-exercise to aid muscle recovery. Glutamine may also support the production of the growth hormone, which helps to improve muscle mass, making it ideal for weight-loss programmes. A key amino acid for the gut, glutamine also helps to repair and nourish the intestines and support immune function. Buy as a powder.

MSM (methylsulfonylmethane) is an organic sulfur compound – an essential nutrient found in the body, playing a critical role in detoxification and in reducing inflammatory conditions. MSM is a beneficial nutrient for bone health, helping arthritis and improving joint flexibility. It has been shown to break down the calcification that is frequently associated with chronic inflammation, particularly in the arteries. It also increases the thickness and strength of nails and hair, and supports healthy skin. Buy as a powder.

Nutritional yeast flakes are formed from deactivated yeast and are a complete protein that is particularly rich in the B vitamins, making it a useful energizing food. Buy in tubs.

Probiotic powders Beneficial bacteria (probiotics) are naturally present in the gut and are vital for overall health, digestion, detoxification, immune function and can even influence our mood. Beneficial bacteria can be easily diminished through stress, medications and a poor diet. Probiotic powders are a convenient way to increase your levels of healthy bacteria.

Shilajit is a brown pitch or tar that exudes from layers of rocks in several mountain ranges of the world, although it is often referred to as a herb. Because it possesses a range of minerals, it is used as a supplement to mineralize the body. It also contains fulvic acid, which aids nutrient absorption as well as being a strong detoxifier. Buy as a powder or capsules.

Tocotrienols Commonly derived from rice bran, this whole food provides a natural, concentrated source of bio-available vitamin E plus other nutrients and plant-based fats important for optimal health benefits. It is rich in antioxidants, B vitamins and minerals and adds a delicious, sweet flavour to a smoothie. Buy as capsules or as a powder.

Zeolite is a natural volcanic mineral and one of the most powerful negatively charged minerals in nature. It is used as a natural chelating agent that allows the release of toxins, pesticides and heavy metals from the body. It is commonly used as a detoxifier. Buy as a liquid or powder.

MAKING SUBSTITUTIONS

The range of supercharged ingredients included in this book is vast. This is to enable you to discover the wealth of ingredients available that have the ability to transform your health and support specific body systems.

There's no denying, however, that some of these can be expensive, but as explained earlier, because they are so nutrient dense and rich in flavour you use them only in very small amounts in each recipe, which means that you will be able to make many drinks from one pack.

In some cases you can substitute different supercharged ingredients for the ones stated in the recipe or simply take one or two of them out of the recipe altogether. You will still benefit from the remaining foods that make up the juice or smoothie, and the drinks will retain their weight-loss-boosting abilities.

When planning your diet programme, decide which supercharged foods you want to purchase. Select a number that appeal to you and incorporate them into the recipes. Use The Quick Look, starting on page 150, to help you.

Here are some substitutions that you can make if you wish:

- Instead of cacao powder, use cocoa powder, but reduce the amount to taste, as it is normally stronger in flavour.
- Instead of camu camu, use baobab powder.
- Instead of chlorella and spirulina, use a green superfood blend, wheatgrass powder, moringa powder or an extra handful of spinach or kale.
- Instead of goji berries, use raisins, or dried cherries or cranberries.
- Instead of incan berries, use raisins or dried cherries.
- Instead of macadamia nuts, use cashew nuts.
- Instead of maqui berry powder, use a handful of blueberries or goji berry powder, acai berry powder or a superberry blend.
- Instead of a tocotrienols capsule, use a vitamin E capsule.
- Try yerbe mate instead of green tea or coffee.

HEALTHY PANTRY STAPLES

All the ingredients for the drinks in this book are chosen for their health benefits. In addition to stocking your cupboards and fridge with fresh foods and key supercharged ingredients, it is worth storing some healthy staples to add flavour and nutrition to your drinks. These include:

Coconut water, which is naturally hydrating and rich in all the electrolytes. Buy in cartons.

Frozen fruit is an economical way of adding natural sweetness to drinks.

Himalayan sea salt can lift the flavour of smoothies and it also provides trace minerals, including magnesium and iodine, which are often at low levels in the average diet.

Natural sweeteners Although the majority of the recipes avoid any additional sweetener, you may find it useful to have some healthy natural sweeteners for some drinks. In addition to manuka or raw honey, bee pollen and yacon, you can add sweetness occasionally with stevia or xylitol. These natural sweeteners are very low in calories, or calorie-free, and will not disrupt blood sugar levels.

Nut and seed butters These add healthy fats, protein and a creamy texture to smoothies. When opened, store them in the fridge.

Nuts and seeds will provide protein, fibre, healthy fats and essential nutrients to smoothies. Store in the fridge after opening the packet.

Spices Chilli, ginger, cinnamon and turmeric not only enhance the flavour of drinks but they also provide a wealth of health benefits. Use fresh root ginger and turmeric (or ground turmeric), fresh chillies and ground cinnamon to increase nourishment and liven up your drinks.

BASIC RECIPES

Kombucha and kefir are nourishing fermented liquids that add gut-friendly probiotics to your drinks. Bone broth is a super-nourishing liquid to add to drinks or use in cooking, and a simple nut milk can be beneficial to take before bedtime.

Cinnamon Nut Milk

Take this optional drink to help balance your blood sugar level at night.

Serves 3

150g/5½oz/1 cup blanched almonds
1 vanilla pod
3 pitted soft dried dates

1 tbsp coconut oil
½ tsp ground cinnamon

Soak the nuts in water overnight, then drain and rinse. Put into a blender or food processor with 750ml/26fl oz/3 cups water.

Cut the vanilla pod in half and scrape the seeds into the blender. (Save the pod for another use.) Add the dates, oil and cinnamon. Blend until smooth and creamy. Pour into glasses and serve. Store in the fridge for up to 24 hours.

Fermented drinks

Including fermented drinks, such as kefir and kombucha, in your juice and smoothie diet is beneficial because they help to support optimal digestive function and immune health, which is vital for overall health. A healthy digestion lowers inflammation and can also reduce levels of circulating leptin – a hunger hormone that influences the appetite. Leptin acts as a switch in your brain to turn hunger signals off, and it reduces body fat – so daily probiotics from these drinks can help you lose weight.

When making the fermented drinks, kefir and kombucha, do not use metal equipment or utensils. Use wooden or plastic spoons, a plastic strainer and plastic or glass bowls.

Home-Made Kefir

Kefir is rich in amino acids, enzymes, calcium, magnesium, phosphorus and B vitamins. It contains several major strains of friendly bacteria (*Lactobacillus caucasus, Leuconostoc, Acetobacter* species and *Streptococcus* species) as well as beneficial yeasts, which can support digestive function and immune health. It is made with kefir 'grains', which are a mother culture. Although cow's milk is typically used, it can be made with sheep's milk, coconut or nut milk. You can also make water kefir using water grains.

Kefir can be made at home or can be purchased in health stores or online. You must use organic full-fat milk for kefir. Either use organic UHT milk or heat pasteurized milk to just below boiling point and cool it before using. You can also make coconut kefir using canned organic full-fat coconut milk (without fillers or additives). Kefir grains can be purchased online.

Milk Kefir

1 sachet of milk kefir grains
1l/35fl oz/4 cups organic full-fat milk or full-fat coconut milk

Put the kefir in a large sterilized glass jar and pour over the milk. Stir well. Cover with a lid, but do not seal, and leave to ferment in a warm place, away from direct sunlight, for at least 24 hours. The milk will separate to form the kefir liquid underneath.

Strain through a sieve and reserve the grains, then start the process again. Store the kefir in the fridge for up to 4 days. If you regularly make kefir with coconut, after 4 or 5 batches you will need to refresh the grains by leaving them in dairy milk for a few days to enable them to feed.

Water Kefir

70g/2½oz/scant ⅓ cup caster sugar
1 sachet of water kefir grains
½ lemon
1 thin slice of fresh ginger, peeled (optional)

Pour 750ml/26fl oz/3 cups filtered, boiled and cooled water (or coconut water) into a glass jar.

Add the sugar and leave to dissolve. Add the remaining ingredients. Cover, but do not seal, and leave to ferment at room temperature for 24–72 hours, depending on the strength you prefer. Strain the water kefir and bottle it in smaller containers. Drink immediately or leave for a further 24 hours to continue fermenting. Re-use the kefir grains to make another batch.

Home-Made Kombucha

Kombucha is made from sweetened tea that's been fermented by bacteria and yeast (known as SCOBY). It is rich in many of the enzymes your body produces for digestion and it aids cleansing and supports liver health. Kombucha also contains glucosamines, which are beneficial for cartilage structure and to prevent arthritis. It is antioxidant rich and is good for immune health. You can buy kombucha online or make your own using a SCOBY starter.

4–6 tea bags, to taste, or 1½ tbsp loose-leaf tea
170g/6oz/¾ cup caster, or granulated sugar or coconut sugar
1 packet of kombucha starter culture (SCOBY)

Put the tea bags in a large sterilized glass container and add the sugar. Pour over 750ml/26fl oz/3 cups boiling water. Stir well and leave the mixture to cool to room temperature. Add the SCOBY.

Cover with a cloth or muslin and leave in a warm place for 3–14 days to brew. The liquid will become a little cloudier when ready. After 3 days, taste the brew. If it tastes fruity and not like tea, it's ready. If not, leave it for another day.

Strain the mixture, but leave a little in the container with the SCOBY to make another batch. Store the brew in the fridge for up to 4 days – it will get fizzier, but it is still fine to drink.

Bone Broth

Calcium, magnesium, phosphorus and other minerals are all contained in bone. It is also rich in gelatine and collagen to support the health of the gut and is useful for lowering inflammation. Any organic bones, such as beef or lamb, can be used, or use a whole chicken carcass instead. The addition of garlic is optional - it not only adds flavour but is a valuable immunity-supporting ingredient too. Use the stock as a drink, to add to a smoothie or as the base for soups, stews, casseroles and other recipes.

700g–1kg/1lb 9oz–2lb 4oz organic beef bones or marrow bones
1 whole head of garlic, cloves peeled (optional)
2 carrots, chopped
1 onion, quartered
2 celery sticks, chopped
1 bay leaf
2 tbsp apple cider vinegar
1 strip of kombu seaweed (optional)
3–4l/105–140fl oz/12–16 cups filtered water

Put all the ingredients in a large flameproof casserole or saucepan with the filtered water to cover. Bring to the boil, then reduce the heat to very low so that the stock is barely simmering. Cover and cook for at least 8 hours and preferably up to 24 hours. Top up with water if needed during cooking. Strain the stock through a sieve. Cool and skim off the fat that has risen to the top. (You can store the fat and use it to cook with.) Store in the fridge for up to 3 days or freeze in batches and use within 1 month.

CHAPTER 1

YOUR SUPERCHARGED THREE-DAY DETOX

The Juice-Cleanse Blitz

The three-day detox is a *juice-only* plan designed for anyone seeking to lose weight or who needs a quick cleanse to revitalize energy levels and kick-start a healthier eating programme. It's also perfect as a quick way to get your body ready for a special occasion or as a periodic cleansing programme to shed excess weight and recharge your vitality.

A three-day juice plan helps to jump-start a weight-loss regime while simultaneously retraining your taste buds to enjoy healthy fruits and vegetables, making it the first step towards a long-lasting lifestyle change. This detox plan will clean your system in readiness for those improved eating patterns to ensure you have a permanently slim, trim and healthy body.

By following this juice cleanse you can lose pounds ultra-fast. Not only will you lose weight, but you'll also find that your energy levels soar and your skin will be clearer and more radiant. It is a carefully designed juicing plan that can help you lose weight more effectively than ever before. It will also supercharge your body with nutrients and enzymes for the ultimate body boost to help you keep weight off permanently.

During each day you will be drinking five juices and a glass of nut milk. This is a low-calorie (600–800kcal) three-day programme to boost weight loss. I recommend that at least one of your juices contains one scoop of protein powder to help support energy levels and healthy muscle mass. If you are particularly active, I recommend that you stir a scoop of protein powder into two to three of the juices each day. This programme is not designed for longer than three days. If you wish to follow a longer programme, please see the guidelines under the Supercharged Diet Week or Supercharged Diet Month programmes.

Be prepared

To get the most benefits from your detox, don't jump right into it without cleaning up your diet beforehand. The week before you intend to start your detox, gradually reduce your intake of coffee and tea, alcohol, processed and convenience foods and ready-meals, sugar and sweeteners, gluten, dairy and red meat except wild game. This will make it easier to follow the plan without having withdrawal symptoms from the foods you normally eat.

Drink 1–2 glasses of hot water with lemon and a slice of ginger each day to hydrate your body and kick-start your digestive system.

Two days before you are due to start on the plan, focus your meals on lean protein (poultry, fish, eggs and wild game) with plenty of vegetables and some fruit. Snack on nuts and seeds if you feel hungry. Include lots of water as well as nut milks, coconut water, coffee alternatives such as dandelion coffee, herbal teas and green tea. Plan ahead by reading the recipes in this chapter and the sample plan opposite and decide which ingredients you need to buy in advance. Re-read The Supercharged Diet Basics starting on page 8 to make sure you are fully prepared. The day before starting, use the shopping list on page 27 to plan what foods you need to buy for your Three-Day Detox to avoid having to pop out to the shops to stock up during the detox itself.

How your plan works

Each morning, start the detox with a glass of hot water with the juice of ½ lemon and, if you wish, add a slice of fresh ginger.

You will be drinking five juices spread throughout each day, plus a glass of nut milk. A serving of juice is approximately 400–500ml/14–17fl oz/1½–2 cups. All the recipes are designed to serve one person, but the exact yield will vary depending on the precise size of the produce you use and the efficiency of your juicer.

As well as the juices, it is important to drink plenty of liquids in the form of herbal teas, hot water with lemon or a slice of peeled root ginger, as well as water at room temperature. I recommend that you drink about 1l/35fl oz/4 cups water a day, which can be in the form of herbal teas. I also suggest you include a glass (measuring about 250ml/9fl oz/1 cup) of coconut water daily to keep your body hydrated. On this page you will find a daily plan, and on page 26 you will find a suggested three-day programme.

What if you are very hungry?

During the three-day detox it is best if you avoid eating and take just the juices I recommend here, plus the additional drinks; however, if you really need something to munch on, reach for some celery or cucumber sticks with a pinch of sea salt or lemon juice. A bowl of warm vegetable broth can also help, and it is especially welcoming if you're detoxing in cold weather.

Blood sugar balance – essential for weight loss and energy

To keep your blood sugar level balanced, the juices in this section focus on vegetables with only a little fruit for sweetness. I also recommend that in the evening you make up a glass of Cinnamon Nut Milk (page 19) to provide additional protein and healthy fat. This can be helpful for stabilizing your blood sugar levels during the night to help promote a good night's sleep. Balancing your blood sugar through the day is important to avoid energy dips and cravings. The addition of protein also helps support muscle mass as you lose weight. For this reason I suggest that you add a scoop of protein powder to one of your drinks during the day.

Rest and exercise

During the plan you'll be ingesting fewer calories and macronutrients, such as protein, carbohydrates and fat, than you usually would. You'll therefore want to ensure you have plenty of rest and sleep, although some light exercise can be beneficial, such as walking, swimming, gentle yoga or Pilates.

The Supercharged Three-Day Detox daily plan

On waking hot water with lemon juice and ginger
Breakfast juice
Mid-morning juice
Lunch juice
Afternoon snack juice
Dinner juice
Bedtime Cinnamon Nut Milk
Throughout the day drink water, 1 glass of coconut water, herbal teas. Add a serving of protein powder to one juice.

Decide on your juice selection

I've suggested a Supercharged Three-Day Detox plan below, but you can pick and choose between the different juices in the pages that follow according to your preference. If you are short of time, select two or three juices and double up so that you are drinking the same juice twice in the day. I do recommend, however, that wherever possible you include a wide variety of juices so that you will be taking in a range of nutrients. I have included a number of supercharged foods, but this does not mean you have to buy and use them all. Many of them are also interchangeable (see Substitutions on page 18).

What to do after the detox

Many people choose to continue with juicing and move onto either the Supercharged Diet Week

Your suggested Supercharged Three-Day Detox juice programme

Day 1

On waking Add the juice of ½ lemon to a 250ml/9fl oz/1 cup glass of hot water, with a thin slice of peeled root ginger, if you like
8am Minted Kale (page 34)
11am Liver Flush (page 32), plus 1 scoop of protein powder
1pm Green Purity (page 30)
3pm Cellulite Buster (page 42)
6pm Anti-inflammatory Green Blend (page 42)
Bedtime Cinnamon Nut Milk (page 19)
Throughout the day Drink 1l/35fl oz/4 cups water and a 250ml/9fl oz/1 cup glass of coconut water, plus herbal teas

Day 2

On waking Add the juice of ½ lemon to a 250ml/9fl oz/1 cup glass of hot water, with a thin slice of peeled root ginger, if you like
8am Deep Green (page 28)
11am Watercress Wonder (page 36), plus 1 scoop of protein powder
1pm Green Roots (page 38)
3pm Asparagus Pick-Me-Up (page 38)
6pm Calm and Soothe (page 40)
Bedtime Cinnamon Nut Milk (page 19)
Throughout the day Drink 1l/35fl oz/4 cups water and a 250ml/9fl oz/1 cup glass coconut water, plus herbal teas

Day 3

On waking Add the juice of ½ lemon to a 250ml/9fl oz/1 cup glass of hot water, with a thin slice of peeled root ginger, if you like
8am Wake-Up Juice (page 40)
11am Enzyme Support (page 32), plus 1 scoop of protein powder
1pm Parsley Perfection (page 28)
3pm Light and Fresh (page 34)
6pm Immune Blast (page 35)
Bedtime Cinnamon Nut Milk (page 19)
Throughout the day Drink 1l/35fl oz/4 cups water and a 250ml/9fl oz/1 cup glass of coconut water, plus herbal teas

or the Supercharged Diet Month to reap further health benefits and to enable them to achieve their weight-loss goal quickly and effectively. Also, refer back to 'Continue to benefit from your diet plan' on page 10 for advice on how to avoid negating the benefits of this detox by making unwholesome choices. Also, you might like to look at 'What if you need to lose more weight?' on page 48 and Your Supercharged Green for Life starting on page 114.

The Supercharged Three-Day Detox shopping list

Fruit:
9 lemons
1 pink grapefruit
3 limes
1 orange
10 green apples
3 ripe pears and 1 Asian pear
1 punnet of fresh blueberries, or 1 small bag of frozen blueberries
1 pineapple (about 550g/1lb 4oz)

Vegetables:
1 bunch of mint
1 bunch of coriander
1 bunch of parsley
1 small bag of spinach leaves
1 pack of kale leaves
1 small green cabbage
1 small red cabbage
1 head of broccoli
1 small pack of rocket leaves
1 cos lettuce
2 little gem lettuces
1 large handful of watercress
9 cucumbers
1 small butternut squash
2 carrots
1 beetroot
1 small celeriac
2 heads of celery
1 fennel bulb
3 tomatoes
1 red pepper
1 small bunch of asparagus
1 small punnet of alfalfa sprouts

The supercharged foods:
(**Note** These can be optional and many are interchangeable – see the recipes and substitutions on page 18)

aloe vera juice
baobab powder
chaga mushroom powder
chlorella powder
coconut oil
flaxseed oil or hempseed oil
glutamine powder
Himalayan sea salt, or sea salt
matcha green tea powder
milk thistle tincture or powder
MSM powder
moringa powder
mulberry leaf powder
nutritional yeast flakes
probiotic powder
protein powder (vegan)
spirulina powder
tocotrienol capsules
wheatgrass powder

High-powered extras:
Tabasco sauce
6cm/2½in piece of root ginger
1cm/½in piece of turmeric root or a small pack of ground turmeric
1l/35fl oz carton coconut water
150g/5½oz/1 cup almonds
1 vanilla pod or ½ tsp vanilla extract
3 soft dried pitted dates
herbal tea bags (optional)

Deep Green

4 mint sprigs
¼ pineapple, skin cut off
1 lemon, peeled
½ cucumber
2 large handfuls of kale leaves
⅛–¼ tsp SPIRULINA powder, to taste

The amazingly nutritious alga, spirulina, gives this minty drink its power. It boasts 60–70 per cent protein, making it ideal for supporting energy during your juice plan. Spirulina is known for its cleansing abilities, thanks to its high chlorophyll content, which helps to remove toxins from the body, making it ideal to be taken in any weight-loss programme.

Put all the ingredients, except the spirulina, through an electric juicer. Stir in the spirulina and serve immediately.

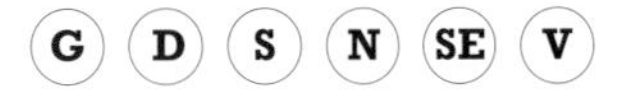

Nutritional information per serving
Kcals 124 | **Protein** 4.6g
Carbohydrates 22.8g, of which sugars 22.8g
Fat 1.6g, of which saturates 0.2g

Parsley Perfection

1 large handful of parsley
1 lemon, peeled
1 cucumber
1 green apple
2 celery sticks
¼ tsp MULBERRY LEAF powder or MORINGA powder

This alkaline green juice is for green lovers everywhere. Parsley is packed with energizing and cleansing chlorophyll, plus vitamins A and C, iron and magnesium, and is a potent cleanser of the kidneys, liver and urinary tract, making it perfect for weight-loss programmes. Stir in a little mulberry leaf powder and you can expect an energy boost.

Put all the ingredients, except the mulberry leaf, through an electric juicer. Stir in the mulberry leaf and serve immediately.

G D S N SE V

Nutritional information per serving
Kcals 83 | **Protein** 4.6g
Carbohydrates 13.1g, of which sugars 12.8g
Fat 1.1g, of which saturates 0g

1cm/½in piece of root ginger
2 celery sticks
1 Asian pear
1 green apple
1 handful of kale
1 lemon, peeled
1 small handful of parsley
½ cucumber
1 TOCOTRIENOLS capsule, squeezed, or ¼ tsp powder or 1 vitamin E capsule
¼ tsp MSM powder
⅛ tsp CHLORELLA powder

Start the day with this weight-loss and purifying sweet juice. The juice is rich in sulfur, an essential mineral that plays an important role in the health of connective tissues, as well as the skin and hair. Including a little chlorella adds extra protein and enhances cleansing while on your weight-loss programme.

Put all the ingredients, except the tocotrienols, MSM and chlorella, through an electric juicer. Stir in the remaining ingredients and serve immediately.

Health Benefits

MSM (methylsulfonylmethane) is a naturally occurring sulfur compound that is essential for soft, beautiful skin. Sulfur is naturally present in certain foods, particularly green leafy vegetables, but it is often low in our diets. Using MSM powder is an effective way to boost your intake of sulfur, which helps to keep skin cells more permeable, flexible and plump. MSM powder is equally beneficial for supporting connective tissue and joint health.

G D S N SE V

Nutritional information per serving
Kcals 121 | **Protein** 4.5g
Carbohydrates 24.4g, of which sugars 23.7g
Fat 1.1g, of which saturates 0.1g

Enzyme Support

1 handful of alfalfa sprouts
½ fennel bulb
1 ripe pear
1 lemon, peeled
1cm/½in piece of root ginger
2 handfuls of spinach leaves
¼ tsp PROBIOTIC powder
100ml/3½fl oz/generous ⅓ cup coconut water

If you're feeling heavy and bloated, this enzyme-packed juice will kick-start your digestion. It's light and refreshing and is perfect in the morning. Fennel is a cleansing vegetable that assists kidney function and eliminates excess fluid from the body. Adding probiotics can help soothe digestive upsets, beat the bloat and boost overall wellness.

Put all the ingredients, except the probiotic powder and coconut water, through an electric juicer. Stir in the probiotic powder and coconut water, and serve immediately.

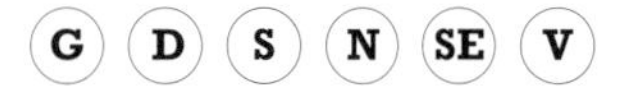

Nutritional information per serving
Kcals 82 | **Protein** 4g
Carbohydrates 14.2g, of which sugars 10.5g
Fat 1g, of which saturates 0.1g

Liver Flush

Pictured>

½ beetroot
3 broccoli florets
1 small cucumber
1 lemon, peeled
1 green apple
5 drops MILK THISTLE tincture or ¼ tsp MILK THISTLE powder

Give your liver a helping hand with this invigorating and cleansing juice. Beetroot juice is an excellent liver cleanse – perfect for helping to shift stubborn fat. It also contains silica for healthy skin, hair, nails and bones. Milk thistle contains a range of antioxidants including silymarin, a flavonoid known to support liver function.

Put all the ingredients, except the milk thistle, through an electric juicer. Stir in the milk thistle and serve immediately.

Nutritional information per serving
Kcals 85 | **Protein** 4.5g
Carbohydrates 14.2g, of which sugars 14g
Fat 0.8g, of which saturates 0.1g

Minted Kale

3 mint sprigs
2 large handfuls of kale leaves
1 cucumber
1 lemon, peeled
1 green apple
¼ tsp WHEATGRASS powder

Make this light and refreshing juice to kick-start your three-day juice plan. Kale is one of the healthiest vegetables there is, and it's a must for any green-juice detox programme. It's rich in glucosinolates, which are converted in the body to form detox-activating chemicals, known as isothiocyanates. These are vital for cleansing and detoxification.

Put all the ingredients, except the wheatgrass, through an electric juicer. Stir in the wheatgrass and serve immediately.

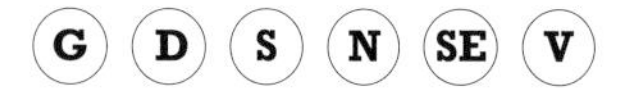

Nutritional information per serving
Kcals 93 | **Protein** 5.6g
Carbohydrates 13.2g, of which sugars 12.4g
Fat 0.2g, of which saturates 0.2g

1 cucumber
2 celery sticks
1 lime, peeled
1 green apple
1 romaine lettuce
½ tsp BAOBAB powder

This blend balances nutritious green vegetables with lime for a light, hydrating and alkalizing juice. The combination of electrolyte-rich veggies is perfect for tackling bloating and getting that enviable flat tummy.

Put all the ingredients, except the baobab, through an electric juicer. Stir in the baobab and serve immediately.

Nutritional information per serving
Kcals 131 | **Protein** 6.6g
Carbohydrates 18.9g, of which sugars 18.7g
Fat 2.5g, of which saturates 0.3g

½ tsp CHAGA MUSHROOM powder
300g/10½oz butternut squash, peeled
2 carrots
1 handful of spinach leaves
1 orange, peeled
½ tsp COCONUT OIL, melted
1 handful of ice cubes

Blast fat and enhance your immune health with this vibrant juice. Traditionally, chaga has been used to support the immune system, promote longevity and preserve youth. The addition of coconut oil helps to energize the body and support a healthy metabolism, boosting weight loss. Butternut squash and carrot are high in vitamin A, which is great for your vision, your skin and your immune system.

Make a tea with the chaga by adding it to 150ml/5fl oz/scant ⅔ cup hot water. Stir and leave to cool. Put the squash, carrots, spinach and orange through an electric juicer. Pour into a blender and add the tea, oil and ice cubes. Process briefly, then serve immediately.

(G) (D) (S) (N) (SE) (V)

Nutritional information per serving
Kcals 243 | **Protein** 6.7g
Carbohydrates 47.8g, of which sugars 37.1g
Fat 2.8g, of which saturates 1.5g

Watercress Wonder

¼ small pineapple, skin cut off
1 large handful of watercress
4 celery sticks
1 green apple
½ cucumber
¼ tsp PROBIOTIC powder
½ tsp GLUTAMINE powder

Nutrient-rich watercress is an excellent health booster and a low-calorie cleansing veggie – ideal for boosting weight loss. It is known to support detoxification and for cleansing the body, and its natural diuretic properties help to shift excess fluid and reduce bloating. The addition of glutamine makes this particularly effective for weight loss.

Put all the ingredients, except the probiotic and glutamine, through an electric juicer. Stir in the probiotic and glutamine, then serve immediately.

Health Benefits

Glutamine is an extremely important dietary supplement for anyone wishing to lose weight. It is an amino acid that is primarily stored in our muscles. By supplementing with glutamine you will preserve muscle mass, which is essential for maintaining a healthy metabolism as you lose weight. Glutamine will also reduce cravings for high-glycaemic carbohydrates – which cause sharp rises followed by drops in blood sugar levels – and it will make your weight-loss programme much easier.

G D S N SE CI V

Nutritional information per serving
Kcals 138 | **Protein** 6.6g
Carbohydrates 27.9g, of which sugars 25.1g

3 asparagus spears
4 broccoli florets
½ cucumber
1 ripe pear
½ lime, peeled
¼ tsp CHLORELLA powder
100ml/3½fl oz/generous ⅓ cup coconut water

A wonderful alkalizing juice, this asparagus and broccoli mix is also rich in B vitamins to promote energy and support detoxification. Asparagus is a diuretic – helping to shift excess fluid and making it perfect for tackling bloating. It is also abundant in an amino acid called asparagine, which helps to cleanse the body of waste.

Put all the ingredients, except the chlorella and coconut water, through an electric juicer. Stir in the chlorella and coconut water, then serve immediately.

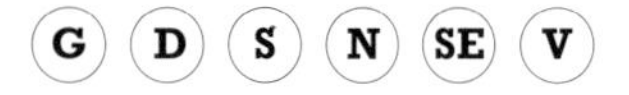

Nutritional information per serving
Kcals 94 | **Protein** 4.7g
Carbohydrates 16.2g, of which sugars 12.6g
Fat 0.9g, of which saturates 0.1g

2 celery sticks
¼ small celeriac root
1 pear
1 lemon, peeled
1cm/½in piece of root ginger
1 handful of coriander leaves
½ cucumber
1 tsp ALOE VERA juice

Light and sweet-tasting celeriac combines with pear and ginger for a fresh and piquant drink. Coriander is a potent natural diuretic, which helps to reduce water retention. It also improves digestion and helps the body get rid of waste products, which is essential for weight loss. Celeriac is a rich source of the electrolytes potassium and sodium, making this ideal for hydrating the body and restoring a healthy fluid balance.

Put all the ingredients, except the aloe vera, through an electric juicer. Stir in the aloe vera and serve immediately.

Nutritional information per serving
Kcals 106 | **Protein** 3.5g
Carbohydrates 19.9g, of which sugars 19.3g
Fat 1.1g, of which saturates 0g

Calm and Soothe

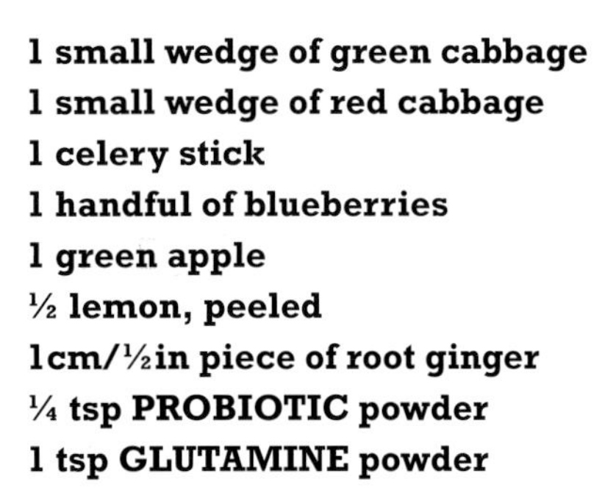

1 small wedge of green cabbage
1 small wedge of red cabbage
1 celery stick
1 handful of blueberries
1 green apple
½ lemon, peeled
1cm/½in piece of root ginger
¼ tsp PROBIOTIC powder
1 tsp GLUTAMINE powder

Cabbage juice is soothing and healing for the digestive tract. It also contains sulforaphane, which supports liver detoxification and lowers inflammation. Excess inflammatory chemicals in the body interfere with insulin function, making it more difficult to shed pounds. Glutamine helps to reduce cravings, to make it easier to stick to the diet plan.

Put all the ingredients, except the probiotic and glutamine, through an electric juicer. Stir in the probiotic and glutamine, and serve immediately.

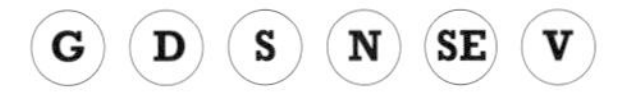

Nutritional information per serving
Kcals 110 | **Protein** 7.2g
Carbohydrates 20.4g, of which sugars 17g
Fat 1.1g, of which saturates 0.1g

Wake-Up Juice

Pictured>

1 large handful of spinach leaves
1 handful of rocket
1 cucumber
1 green apple
1 lime, peeled
4 mint sprigs
⅛ tsp MATCHA GREEN TEA powder

Freshen up your digestive system and kick-start your energy for the day with this leafy juice, packed with nutritious greens and hydrating cucumber. The addition of matcha green tea helps boost fat-burning. Matcha contains the amino acid L-theanine, which, together with matcha's caffeine content, boosts your alertness and improves concentration.

Put all the ingredients, except the matcha, through an electric juicer. Stir in the matcha and serve immediately.

Nutritional information per serving
Kcals 96 | **Protein** 7g
Carbohydrates 14.2g, of which sugars 13.9g
Fat 1.1g, of which saturates 0.1g

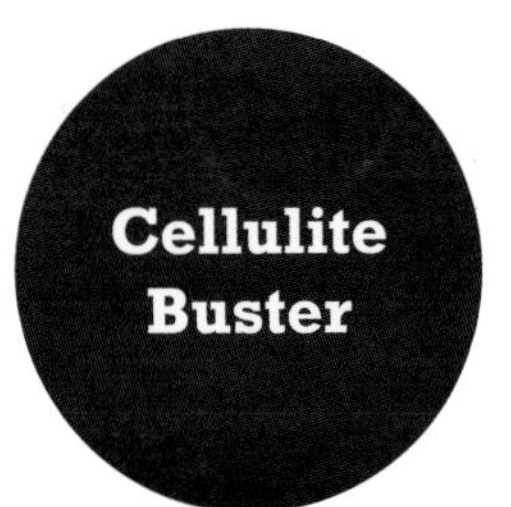

1 pink grapefruit, peeled
2 celery sticks
½ cucumber
1 handful of parsley
2 mint sprigs
¼ tsp MORINGA powder

Rev up your metabolism and stimulate fat-burning to help shift unwanted fat with this light and tangy juice. It includes protein-rich moringa, which contains all the essential amino acids needed by the body and vital for supporting the detoxification processes. The juice is also high in antioxidants to help protect and nourish the skin, plus sulfur – important for the production of collagen, which helps your skin look plump and glowing.

Put all the ingredients, except the moringa, through an electric juicer. Stir in the moringa and serve immediately.

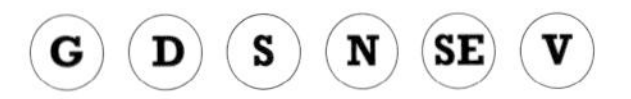

Nutritional information per serving
Kcals 69 | **Protein** 2.9g
Carbohydrates 12.9g, of which sugars 12.9g
Fat 0.5g, of which saturates 0g

Anti-inflammatory Green Blend

¼ small pineapple, skin cut off
1cm/½in piece of root ginger
1 handful of parsley
2 little gem lettuces
½ lemon, peeled
1 green apple
2 celery sticks
1cm/½in piece of TURMERIC ROOT or ¼ tsp ground TURMERIC
1 tbsp PLAIN or VANILLA PROTEIN powder
¼ tsp FLAXSEED OIL

Grab this fabulous juice after exercising. It's packed with anti-inflammatory ingredients turmeric and pineapple, and protein powder to boost muscle recovery during your weight-loss programme.

Put all the ingredients, except the ground turmeric, if using, the protein powder and oil, through an electric juicer. Stir in the ground turmeric and protein powder, and drizzle in the oil, then serve immediately.

Nutritional information per serving
Kcals 214 | **Protein** 17.6g
Carbohydrates 28g, of which sugars 27.5g
Fat 3.6g, of which saturates 0.3g

1 large handful of spinach leaves
3 tomatoes
2 celery sticks
½ cucumber
1 red pepper
½ lime, peeled
a dash of Tabasco sauce (optional)
a pinch of nori flakes (optional)
a pinch of Himalayan sea salt or sea salt, or to taste
1 tsp NUTRITIONAL YEAST FLAKES
¼ tsp FLAXSEED OIL or HEMPSEED OIL

Keeping the sugar content low during your detox plan is important for effective weight loss. This is a fabulous vegetable combination, which is cleansing and hydrating, plus it's low in calories. It's a good source of electrolytes to refresh your body and maintain a healthy fluid balance. Nutritional yeast flakes are added for their energizing B vitamins, and the omega-rich oil is an easy way to boost your intake of anti-inflammatory fats, which have been shown to support metabolism and weight loss.

Put the spinach, tomatoes, celery, cucumber, pepper and lime through an electric juicer. Stir in the remaining ingredients, or transfer the juice to a blender or food processor and blend until smooth. Serve immediately.

(G) (D) (S) (N) (V)

Nutritional information per serving
Kcals 131 | **Protein** 5.6g
Carbohydrates 18.2g, of which sugars 17.6g
Fat 3.6g, of which saturates 0.5g

CHAPTER 2

YOUR SUPERCHARGED DIET WEEK

A Trimmer Body in Seven Days

The seven-day plan is a *juice and smoothie* programme aimed at anyone who is seeking effective weight loss. It will also deeply cleanse your body, improve digestion and promote a cleaner, clearer body and mind. By focusing solely on juices and smoothies, you will find it an effective way to lose a more significant amount of weight as well as promoting energy.

You will need to set aside a period of time when you can commit to drinking green vegetable-based juices and smoothies only, in order to regain vitality, lose weight and get your body back into balance. As you will not be consuming meals, except for the odd snack or soup, your overall calorie intake will be significantly reduced.

To enable effective weight loss it is important to consume a selection of the smoothies that contain protein and healthy fats in order to support healthy blood sugar levels and promote sensible weight loss. If you are particularly active, I recommend that you consume more smoothies throughout the day (three smoothies) to sustain your energy.

Many people find it easier to start the programme over a weekend when they have more time to get organized, but it is ideal for following while you are working because being busy can take your mind off food, thereby making it easier to stick to the diet.

Spending a whole week sipping nutrient-dense juices and smoothies is an incredibly invigorating experience, and your body will feel refreshed and rejuvenated afterwards – and, of course, lighter.

Be prepared

If you haven't moved on from the three-day detox, spend some time cleaning up your diet before you start the Supercharged Diet Week to get the most benefits. The week before you intend to start your detox, gradually reduce your intake of coffee and tea, alcohol, processed and convenience foods and ready-meals, sugar and sweeteners, gluten, dairy and red meat except wild game. This will make it easier to follow the plan without having withdrawal symptoms from the foods you normally eat.

Drink 1–2 glasses of hot water with lemon and a slice of ginger each day to hydrate your body and kick-start your digestive system.

Two days before you are due to start on the plan, focus your meals on lean protein (poultry, fish, eggs and wild game) with plenty of vegetables and some fruit. Snack on nuts and seeds if you feel hungry. Include lots of water as well as nut milks, coconut water, coffee alternatives such as dandelion coffee, herbal teas and green tea.

Plan ahead by reading the recipes in this chapter and the sample plan opposite and decide which ingredients you need to buy. Re-read The Supercharged Diet Basics starting on page 8 to make sure you are fully prepared.

How your plan works

Each morning, start the plan with a glass of hot water with the juice of ½ lemon and, if you wish, add a slice of fresh ginger.

You will be drinking three juices and two smoothies (or three if you are very active) spread throughout each day. The smoothies provide more protein and healthy fats than the juices and are more sustaining. If you are very active, choose three smoothies and reduce your juices accordingly. A serving of juice or smoothie is approximately 400–500ml/14–17fl oz/1½–2 cups. All the recipes are designed to serve one person, but the precise yield will vary depending on the size of the produce you use and the efficiency of your juicer.

As well as the juices and smoothies, it is also important to drink plenty of liquids in the form of herbal teas, hot water with lemon or a slice of ginger, as well as water at room temperature. I recommend that you drink about 1l/35fl oz/4 cups water a day, which can be in the form of herbal teas. I also suggest you include a glass (measuring about 250ml/9fl oz/1 cup) of coconut water daily to keep your body hydrated.

What if you are very hungry?

During the seven-day plan it is best if you avoid eating and take just the juices and smoothies I recommend here, plus the additional drinks; however, if you feel very hungry you can include a colourful vegetable salad at lunch or snack on some celery or cucumber sticks with a pinch of sea salt or lemon juice. A bowl of warm vegetable soup can also help, and it is especially welcoming if you're dieting in cold weather.

The first three days of any juice and smoothie programme are typically the hardest, but if you persevere you'll find that your energy and mood will improve. Each day you will be including a smoothie with added protein. As well as aiding weight loss, this helps you to feel full. You should therefore find it easier to stick to the programme as well as noticing significant weight loss.

Protein and blood sugar balance – essential for weight loss and energy

To keep your blood sugar balanced, in addition to including vegetable-based drinks, the smoothies include higher levels of protein than in the three-day detox. Protein is essential for supporting healthy muscle mass, keeping you feeling fuller for longer and avoiding energy dips. By including two smoothies a day, you will consume important protein and healthy fats to keep your energy levels high and to maintain healthy muscle mass as you lose weight. This will support a healthier and more effective longer-term weight loss.

Choose a selection of juices and smoothies each day to ensure a variety of nutrients and supercharged ingredients. If you are short of time, you can make up a double batch of one or two juices or smoothies and store them in the fridge until required.

The Supercharged Diet Week daily plan

On waking hot water with lemon juice and ginger
Breakfast juice
Mid-morning juice
Lunch smoothie and an optional colourful vegetable salad
Mid-afternoon juice
Dinner smoothie
Bedtime optional Cinnamon Nut Milk
Throughout the day drink water, 1 glass of coconut water, herbal teas.

Rest and exercise

During the plan you'll be ingesting fewer calories and macronutrients such as protein, carbohydrates and fat than you usually would. You'll therefore want to ensure you have plenty of rest and sleep, although some light exercise can be beneficial, such as walking, swimming, gentle yoga or Pilates.

Decide on your juice and smoothie selection

Look through the juices and smoothies in this chapter and select a variety each day. Use the following suggested days to guide you. If you do not have time to juice through the day, you can select some of the juices and smoothies and make up a double batch and store it in the fridge. To help stabilize blood sugar overnight, take the optional nut milk, or, if you are really hungry, make up another smoothie. You can choose any drink from this or any other chapter in this book.

What to do after the plan

Your programme does not stop here. If you have moderate or significant weight-loss goals, you may wish to consider the Supercharged Diet Month starting on page 72. Otherwise, try to include a juice or smoothie each day as an easy breakfast option or a mid-morning snack – this is a great way to enjoy a greater variety of vegetables and nutrients in your diet. Also, refer back to 'Continue to benefit from your diet plan' on page 10 and look at Your Supercharged Green for Life starting on page 114.

What if you need to lose more weight?

After the plan, if you wish to lose weight, limit your intake of starchy carbohydrates to one small portion a day (the equivalent of 125ml/4fl oz/½ cup in volume of cooked starchy vegetables) and focus on the following: pumpkin, butternut squash, beetroot, carrots or sweet potato, or the equivalent of 80ml/2½fl oz/⅓ cup in volume of cooked wholegrain rice or quinoa, or 2 oatcakes.

Ditch all white refined carbohydrates and sweetened processed foods and drinks. Watch your intake of caffeine and alcohol too, as these can cause fluctuations in blood sugar levels, affecting energy and triggering cravings, which may result in weight gain.

Your suggested Supercharged Diet Week

Day 1

On waking Add the juice of ½ lemon to a 250ml/9fl oz/1 cup glass of hot water, with a thin slice of peeled root ginger, if you like

Breakfast Gut Healer (page 54)

Mid-morning Red-Carpet Cleanse (page 56)

Lunch Muscle Booster (page 65) and an optional colourful vegetable salad

Mid-afternoon Longevity Nectar (page 57)

Dinner Chocolate Fix (page 68)

Bedtime Optional Cinnamon Nut Milk (page 19)

Throughout the day Drink 1l/35fl oz/4 cups

water and a 250ml/9fl oz/1 cup glass of coconut water, plus herbal teas

Day 2
On waking Lemon and water, as Day 1
Breakfast Hormone Cleanse (page 60)
Mid-morning Protein Boost (page 58)
Lunch Matcha Fat Burner (page 68) and an optional colourful vegetable salad
Mid-afternoon Minty Lettuce (page 50)
Dinner Vanilla Cashew Cream (page 65)
Bedtime Optional Cinnamon Nut Milk (page 19)
Throughout the day Additional drinks, as Day 1

Day 3
On waking Lemon and water, as Day 1
Breakfast Kale Supreme (page 56)
Mid-morning Rockin' Beetroot Boost (page 54)
Lunch Beauty Detox (page 66) and an optional colourful vegetable salad
Mid-afternoon Sweet Liver Cleanse (page 50)
Dinner Get the Glow (page 70)
Bedtime Optional Cinnamon Nut Milk (page 19)
Throughout the day Additional drinks, as Day 1

Day 4
On waking Lemon and water, as Day 1
Breakfast Protein Pick-Me-Up (page 52)
Mid-morning Spring Freshen-Up (page 58)
Lunch Spinach Energizer (page 70) and an optional colourful vegetable salad
Mid-afternoon Protein Boost (page 58)
Dinner Chocolate Fix (page 68)
Bedtime Optional Cinnamon Nut Milk (page 19)
Throughout the day Additional drinks, as Day 1

Day 5
On waking Lemon and water, as Day 1
Breakfast Invigorate (page 64)
Mid-morning Easy Greens (page 64)
Lunch Matcha Fat Burner (page 68) and an optional colourful vegetable salad
Mid-afternoon Skin Nourish (page 62)
Dinner Muscle Booster (page 65)
Bedtime Optional Cinnamon Nut Milk (page 19)
Throughout the day Additional drinks, as Day 1

Day 6
On waking Lemon and water, as Day 1
Breakfast Power Immune Greens (page 62)
Mid-morning Hormone Cleanse (page 60)
Lunch Vanilla Cashew Cream (page 65) and an optional colourful vegetable salad
Mid-afternoon Protein Boost (page 58)
Dinner Beauty Detox (page 66)
Bedtime Optional Cinnamon Nut Milk (page 19)
Throughout the day Additional drinks, as Day 1

Day 7
On waking Lemon and water, as Day 1
Breakfast Spring Freshen-Up (page 58)
Mid-morning Red-Carpet Cleanse (page 56)
Lunch Get the Glow (page 70) and an optional colourful vegetable salad
Mid-afternoon Longevity Nectar (page 57)
Dinner Chocolate Fix (page 68)
Bedtime Optional Cinnamon Nut Milk (page 19)
Throughout the day Additional drinks, as Day 1

Sweet Liver Cleanse

1 small wedge of dark green cabbage
5cm/2in piece of daikon (mooli/white radish)
1 pear
1 lemon, peeled
½ small sweet potato
1 tsp YACON syrup
a pinch of ground cinnamon, or to taste

Daikon root is a large Asian radish that is rich in sulfur and recognized to aid bile flow in the liver and for supporting digestion. This makes daikon ideal to include in weight-loss plans, because efficient digestion and elimination are essential for losing weight. Yacon syrup is a healthy natural sweetener and prebiotic, enhancing this juice's digestive qualities.

Put all the ingredients, except the yacon syrup and cinnamon, through an electric juicer. Stir in the yacon syrup and cinnamon, and serve immediately.

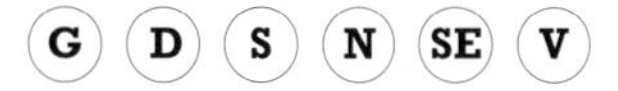

Nutritional information per serving
Kcals 219 | **Protein** 5g
Carbohydrates 50g, of which sugars 26.2g
Fat 1.2g, of which saturates 0.3g

Minty Lettuce

1 tbsp GOJI BERRIES
leaves from 5 mint sprigs
½ romaine lettuce
6 strawberries, hulled
½ fennel bulb
½ lemon, peeled
½ cucumber
½ green apple

Strawberries and mint make this a refreshingly sweet, clean-tasting juice. Goji berries have longevity and strength-building properties and are rich in protein. They also add soluble fibre to balance blood sugar levels, which is important for reducing cravings.

Soak the goji berries in 100ml/3½ fl oz/generous ⅓ cup warm water for 5–10 minutes until softened. Put the remaining ingredients through an electric juicer. Transfer to a blender or food processor and add the goji berries and their soaking liquid. Blend until smooth, then serve.

Nutritional information per serving
Kcals 123 | **Protein** 4.3g
Carbohydrates 21.7g, of which sugars 20.6g
Fat 1.9g, of which saturates 0.2g

1 handful of basil leaves
1 large handful of spinach leaves
1 cucumber
1 lime, peeled
2 celery sticks
1 green apple
¼ tsp MATCHA GREEN TEA powder
¼ tsp SPIRULINA
1 tbsp PLAIN or VANILLA PROTEIN powder
4 ice cubes

Blend this juice with ice to make it extra refreshing. The matcha green tea powder will give you an immediate lift while boosting metabolism and weight loss. To stabilize blood sugar, this juice includes protein powder and spirulina, which is naturally rich in protein and, thanks to its high chlorophyll content, will energize your whole body.

Put all the ingredients, except the matcha, spirulina, protein and ice, through an electric juicer. Transfer to a blender or food processor and add the remaining ingredients. Blend briefly, then serve immediately.

Health Benefits
Matcha green tea is a fabulous metabolism booster, making it a wonderful supercharged ingredient on any weight-loss programme. It is also rich in L-theanine, an amino acid that promotes a state of relaxation and focus by supporting cognitive function. Although green tea does contain a little caffeine, the combination of ingredients promotes concentration and clarity of mind without any of the nervous energy found in coffee.

G D S N SE V

Nutritional information per serving
Kcals 157 | **Protein** 15.1g
Carbohydrates 17.5g, of which sugars 14.3g
Fat 2.7g, of which saturates 0.1g

Rockin' Beetroot Boost

1 beetroot
2 carrots
1 green apple
1 handful of parsley
1 lemon, peeled
1cm/½in piece of root ginger
¼ red chilli, preferably jalapeño
½ tsp SUPERBERRY powder or GOJI BERRY powder

Liver cleansing, kidney supporting and metabolism boosting, this is a fabulous juice to speed up weight loss. The addition of jalapeño chilli and ginger brings a fiery zip to the juice, plus it helps to increase the body's circulation and fat-burning. A little superberry powder adds an extra antioxidant hit.

Put all the ingredients, except the superberry, through an electric juicer. Stir in the superberry and serve immediately.

(G) (D) (S) (N) (SE) (V)

Nutritional information per serving
Kcals 138 | **Protein** 3.2g
Carbohydrates 29.2g, of which sugars 27.1g
Fat 0.9g, of which saturates 0.2g

½ fennel bulb
1 romaine lettuce
4 celery sticks
1 small handful of parsley
1 lime, peeled
1 green apple
1 tsp GLUTAMINE powder

Soothing fennel makes the base for this digestion-friendly juice. Glutamine is included because it is anti-inflammatory and an essential amino acid that is necessary for the growth and repair of the gut lining. It's also useful to support blood sugar and reduce cravings, making it an effective weight-loss aid.

Put all the ingredients, except the glutamine, through an electric juicer. Stir in the glutamine and serve immediately.

Nutritional information per serving
Kcals 117 | **Protein** 8.7g
Carbohydrates 18.3g, of which sugars 14.6g
Fat 2.4g, of which saturates 0.3g

Red-Carpet Cleanse

3 carrots
1 small orange, peeled
½ lime, peeled
1cm/½in piece of root ginger
4 kale leaves
1 tsp GOJI BERRIES
1 tsp COLLAGEN powder
¼ tsp BAOBAB powder
½ tsp COCONUT OIL
1 tbsp coconut flakes

Look special by taking this fabulous juice. Collagen, boosted by vitamin C in the baobab, nourishes your skin and helps to balance blood sugar, making it perfect for weight loss. The carotenes in the carrots help to heal the skin.

Put the carrots, orange, lime, ginger and kale through an electric juicer. Transfer to a blender or food processor and add the remaining ingredients. Blend until smooth and creamy, then serve immediately.

G D S N

Nutritional information per serving
Kcals 235 | **Protein** 8g
Carbohydrates 35.3g, of which sugars 33.8g
Fat 6.7g, of which saturates 4.8g

2 handfuls of kale leaves
1 pear
4 celery sticks
1 lime, peeled
½ cucumber
1cm/½in piece of root ginger
½ tsp BAOBAB powder

Drink this during the day to refresh and recharge your body as you detox. A dash of baobab powder is added to revitalize flagging energy levels. Rich in vitamin C, baobab is a powerful immune booster and also helps to increase the absorption of iron from leafy greens.

Put all the ingredients, except the baobab, through an electric juicer. Stir in the baobab and serve immediately.

G D S N SE V

Nutritional information per serving
Kcals 87 | **Protein** 3.9g
Carbohydrates 13.9g, of which sugars 13.7g
Fat 1.4g, of which saturates 0.1g

Longevity Nectar

4 romaine lettuce leaves
1 green apple
½ cucumber
1 handful of spinach leaves
3 asparagus spears
½ lime, peeled
1cm/½in piece of root ginger
¼ tsp ROYAL JELLY POWDER or BEE POLLEN

Drink this nourishing nectar to keep you looking and feeling young. Royal jelly helps to nourish your adrenal glands. Promoting adrenal health can boost weight loss by improving thyroid function and blood sugar balance. Take the juice daily to increase your mental clarity, energy and overall well-being.

Put all the ingredients, except the royal jelly, through an electric juicer. Stir in the royal jelly and serve immediately.

G D S N SE

Nutritional information per serving
Kcals 72 | **Protein** 3.7g
Carbohydrates 11.8g, of which sugars 11g
Fat 0.9g, of which saturates 0.2g

Spring Freshen-Up

1½ pears
½ cucumber
1 handful of spring greens
1 handful of spinach leaves
1 lemon, peeled
1cm/½in piece of root ginger
¼ tsp CHLORELLA powder

Cucumber, pears and greens make a great morning juice to wake up your digestive system, kick-start cleansing and fill you with energy for the day. Adding a little spicy ginger will perk up your body, and chlorella powder provides energizing chlorophyll and protein to support your weight-loss programme.

Put all the ingredients, except the chlorella, through an electric juicer. Stir in the chlorella and serve immediately.

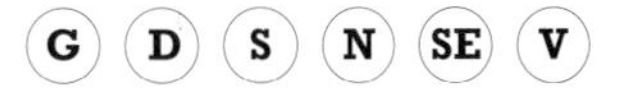

Nutritional information per serving
Kcals 77 | **Protein** 3.3g
Carbohydrates 14.2g, of which sugars 14.2g
Fat 0.7g, of which saturates 0.1g

Protein Boost

Pictured>

1 carrot
1 cucumber
2 celery sticks
2 chard or kale leaves
1 handful of spinach leaves
4 parsley sprigs
1 lemon, peeled
¼ tsp SPIRULINA
1 tsp CHIA SEEDS

Carrot adds sweetness to this hard-core green juice. Lemon helps to lighten the juice as well as providing vitamin C to invigorate and cleanse the body. Adding a little spirulina and some chia seeds is a quick way to boost the protein and to add soluble fibre, which will help to stabilize your blood sugar while you lose weight.

Put all the ingredients, except the spirulina and chia seeds, through an electric juicer. Stir in the spirulina and chia seeds, and leave for 5 minutes. Stir to incorporate the chia seeds and serve immediately.

Nutritional information per serving
Kcals 116 | **Protein** 5.7g
Carbohydrates 16.7g, of which sugars 14g
Fat 2.7g, of which saturates 0.3g

Hormone Cleanse

2 pears
2 celery sticks
5 broccoli florets
1cm/½in piece of root ginger
½ lemon, peeled
1 tsp CHIA SEEDS
½ tsp PROBIOTIC powder
¼ tsp MORINGA powder

Health in a glass! Drink this light, refreshing blend to cleanse, kick-start your metabolism and recharge your body. Adding a spoonful of chia seeds helps to promote bowel health and the excretion of toxins – essential on a weight-loss programme. Moringa powder provides a wealth of nutrients to support energy levels and it is power-packed with antioxidants for glowing skin.

Put all the ingredients, except the chia, probiotic and moringa, through an electric juicer. Transfer to a blender or food processor and add the remaining ingredients. Blend until smooth, then serve immediately.

Health Benefits

Broccoli and other cruciferous vegetables have high levels of glucosinolates, which help the detoxification of toxins and hormones, including oestrogen. A healthy gut flora is also important to ensure the excretion of oestrogens, and studies have shown that our gut flora has a profound effect on how we metabolize foods. By restoring healthy gut flora, you promote elimination and effective weight loss.

G D S N V

Nutritional information per serving
Kcals 111 | **Protein** 4g
Carbohydrates 19.6g, of which sugars 17.9g
Fat 1.9g, of which saturates 0.2g

4 romaine lettuce leaves
1 Asian pear
1 handful of spinach leaves
1 handful of kale leaves
1 lemon, peeled
1 small handful of parsley
1 cucumber
1 tsp COLLAGEN powder
¼ tsp MSM powder

A cleansing and hydrating combination, this juice is rich in vitamin C to augment the production of collagen in the skin and to promote cell reproduction and repair. MSM powder supports detoxification as well as promoting healthy skin and hair, helping to reduce your toxic load and enabling your body to function optimally to boost weight loss.

Put all the ingredients, except the collagen and MSM, through an electric juicer. Stir in the collagen and MSM, and serve the juice immediately.

G D S N SE

Nutritional information per serving
Kcals 114 | **Protein** 12.2g
Carbohydrates 16.2g, of which sugars 14.1g
Fat 1.3g, of which saturates 0.1g

Power Immune Greens

2 handfuls of kale leaves
1 green apple
4 celery sticks
1 handful of fresh or frozen blueberries
1 handful of fresh or frozen blackberries
4 mint sprigs
¼ cucumber
1 tsp ELDERBERRY tincture or ½ tsp GOJI BERRY powder

Here, a deliciously sweet juice is packed with antioxidants and cleansing greens. It's a great drink to pick up flagging energy levels through the day, making it easier to stick to the diet plan. Elderberry is packed with lots of vitamin C, and is known for its anti-viral and immune-supporting properties. Alternatively, stir in a little goji berry powder for a power-packed juice.

Put all the ingredients, except the elderberry, through an electric juicer. Stir in the elderberry and serve immediately.

Nutritional information per serving
Kcals 87 | **Protein** 3.8g
Carbohydrates 15.1g, of which sugars 13.9g
Fat 1.3g, of which saturates 0.1g

1 cucumber
2 celery sticks
1 handful of spinach leaves
½ lemon, peeled
¼ tsp WHEATGRASS powder or GREEN SUPERFOOD blend

Wheatgrass powder is a fabulous weight-loss aid. It adds nutrient intensity to this light juice while boosting detoxification. You need only a little to increase your vitamin and mineral intake and benefit from its cleansing power.

Put all the ingredients, except the wheatgrass, through an electric juicer. Stir in the wheatgrass and serve immediately.

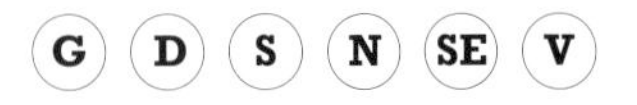

Nutritional information per serving
Kcals 63 | **Protein** 4.4g
Carbohydrates 7.9g, of which sugars 6.7g
Fat 0.8g, of which saturates 0.1g

2 carrots
¼ small pineapple, skin cut off
1cm/½in piece of root ginger
2 handfuls of spinach leaves
a pinch of ground cinnamon
½ tsp MACA powder
100ml/3½fl oz/generous ⅓ cup coconut water

Keep your energy high as you detox with this refreshing juice. Maca powder is an adaptogenic herb, known to strengthen the body and help to maintain optimal stamina and endurance. It is ideal as a cleansing and caffeine-free energizer.

Put all the ingredients, except the cinnamon, maca and coconut water, through an electric juicer. Stir in the remaining ingredients, or transfer the juice to a blender or food processor and blend to combine. Serve the juice immediately.

Nutritional information per serving
Kcals 150 | **Protein** 4.1g
Carbohydrates 30g, of which sugars 24.5g
Fat 1.4g, of which saturates 0.3g

Vanilla Cashew Cream

½ banana, peeled
1 tsp vanilla extract or 1 vanilla pod
1 handful of frozen mixed berries
1 tbsp cashew nuts
1 tbsp GOJI BERRIES
2 tsp COLLAGEN powder
1 handful of spinach leaves, chopped
125ml/4fl oz/½ cup almond or coconut milk

The goji berries in this smoothie supply essential amino acids and plenty of wrinkle-busting, immune-supporting vitamin C to complement the collagen powder in this energy-boosting mix.

Chop the banana and put it into a freezer bag. Exclude all the air, then seal and freeze overnight or until solid. Put the banana into a blender or food processor. If using a vanilla pod, cut the pod in half and scrape the seeds into the blender (save the pod for another use), or add the extract. Add the remaining ingredients and blend until smooth and creamy. Serve immediately.

Nutritional information per serving
Kcals 269 | **Protein** 15.2g
Carbohydrates 30.7g, of which sugars 21.6g
Fat 9.8g, of which saturates 1.5g

Muscle Booster

1 handful of kale leaves, chopped
1 handful of spinach leaves, chopped
¼ ripe avocado, peeled and chopped
1 tsp shelled HEMP SEEDS
½ cucumber, chopped
½ lemon, peeled
250ml/9fl oz/1 cup coconut water
30g/1oz/scant ¼ cup VANILLA PROTEIN powder
½ tsp BEE POLLEN, or MANUKA or RAW HONEY

During any juice programme it is essential to obtain sufficient protein to maintain healthy muscle mass and to support the different phases of detoxification. This drink will maintain even blood sugar levels and keep energy levels high. For a little sweetness, I have added some bee pollen – it's a fabulous supercharged food to boost vitality.

Put all the ingredients into a blender or food processor and blend until smooth and creamy. Serve immediately.

Nutritional information per serving
Kcals 276 | **Protein** 28.5g
Carbohydrates 17.5g, of which sugars 5.2g
Fat 10.3g, of which saturates 1.3g

½ romaine lettuce, chopped
1 celery stick, chopped
½ green apple, cored and chopped
½ pear, cored and chopped
1 tbsp INCAN berries
1 tsp CHIA SEEDS
juice of ½ lemon
1 TOCOTRIENOLS capsule, squeezed, or ¼ tsp powder or 1 vitamin E capsule
1 tsp LUCUMA powder
1 tsp GREEN SUPERFOOD blend
1 tbsp PLAIN or VANILLA PROTEIN powder
200ml/7fl oz/scant 1 cup water or coconut water

Help your body to get stronger and more beautiful inside and out as you lose weight. This smoothie includes fruit and supercharged ingredients to nourish your skin, support cleansing and hydrate your body. It's light and refreshing – perfect for getting you beach-body ready.

Put all the ingredients into a blender or food processor and blend until smooth and creamy. Serve immediately.

Health Benefits
Tocotrienols are added for their muscle-boosting, tissue-regenerating and toxin-cleansing properties. Incan berries are rich in fibre and protective antioxidants, plus iron to keep you energized. Chia seeds contain skin-healthy omega-3 fats and protein – valuable for nourishing the skin – while the addition of green superfood powder supports cleansing.

G D S N CI V

Nutritional information per serving
Kcals 157 | **Protein** 15.3g
Carbohydrates 27.1g, of which sugars 16.9g
Fat 2.1g, of which saturates 0.1g

Chocolate Fix

½ banana, peeled
2 tsp almond nut butter
250ml/9fl oz/1 cup almond milk
30g/1oz/scant ¼ cup VANILLA or CHOCOLATE PROTEIN powder
1 tbsp RAW CACAO powder
1 handful of spinach leaves, chopped
2 pitted soft dried dates, chopped
½ tsp ground cinnamon
¼ tsp CHLORELLA powder or 4 CHLORELLA tablets
2–4 ice cubes

For chocolate lovers, this is an indulgent-tasting smoothie, making it easy to stick to the diet plan. It's filling and satisfying to help you conquer any food cravings.

Chop the banana and put it into a freezer bag. Exclude all the air, then seal and freeze overnight or until solid. Put the banana into a blender or food processor and add the remaining ingredients – using 4 ice cubes if you want a longer, cooler drink. Blend until smooth and creamy. Serve immediately.

Nutritional information per serving
Kcals 394 | **Protein** 30.8g
Carbohydrates 40g, of which sugars 18.3g
Fat 11.8g, of which saturates 1.3g

Matcha Fat Burner

Pictured>

3 Brazil nuts
1 tbsp HEMP SEEDS
125ml/4fl oz/½ cup almond milk
125ml/4fl oz/½ cup coconut water
¼ small pineapple, skin cut off
1 handful of kale leaves, chopped
¼ tsp MATCHA GREEN TEA powder

This amazing smoothie is sweet and nourishing and a fabulous fat-burning blend. Brazil nuts are rich in selenium, which is essential for healthy thyroid function. Matcha green tea powder is a concentrated source of catechins, whose thermogenic (heat-producing) properties promote fat-burning. Studies show that exercising after drinking matcha tea can further boost fat-burning, making this an excellent pre-workout drink.

Put all the ingredients into a blender or food processor and blend until smooth and creamy. Serve immediately.

Nutritional information per serving
Kcals 262 | **Protein** 11.2g
Carbohydrates 25.3g, of which sugars 14.9g
Fat 13.6g, of which saturates 1.6g

1 tbsp pumpkin seeds
1 tbsp COLLAGEN powder, or PLAIN or VANILLA PROTEIN powder
250ml/9fl oz/1 cup coconut milk
1 large handful of frozen mixed berries or blueberries
4 mint sprigs
1 handful of spinach leaves, chopped
1 tbsp lemon juice
1 tsp COCONUT OIL
2 drops stevia, or ½ tsp MANUKA or RAW HONEY, to taste
1 tsp LUCUMA powder
½ tsp ACAI BERRY powder, or GOJI BERRY powder or SUPERBERRY powder
½ tsp MULBERRY LEAF powder

Create an instant detox blend to speed up cleansing, make your skin glow and help you get that slim body you long for.

Put all the ingredients into a blender or food processor and blend until smooth and creamy. Serve immediately.

(G) (D) (S)

Nutritional information per serving
Kcals 293 | **Protein** 17.5g
Carbohydrates 19.8g, of which sugars 11.4g
Fat 15.8g, of which saturates 3.7g

1 banana, peeled
1 tbsp VANILLA PROTEIN powder or COLLAGEN powder
1 large handful of spinach leaves, chopped
1 kiwi fruit, peeled and chopped
300ml/10½fl oz/scant 1¼ cups coconut water
1 tsp CHIA SEEDS
1 tsp COCONUT OIL
½ tsp BAOBAB powder

A creamy banana base, with a hint of kiwi fruit, makes a tasty combination with spinach for a hydrating, alkalizing and energizing smoothie. Chia seeds and coconut oil help to maintain energy.

Chop the banana and put it into a freezer bag. Exclude all the air, then seal and freeze overnight or until solid. Put the banana into a blender or food processor and add the remaining ingredients. Blend until smooth and creamy. Serve immediately.

(G) (D) (S) (N) (CI) (V)

Nutritional information per serving
Kcals 238 | **Protein** 16g
Carbohydrates 29g, of which sugars 14.6g
Fat 6.5g, of which saturates 2.8g

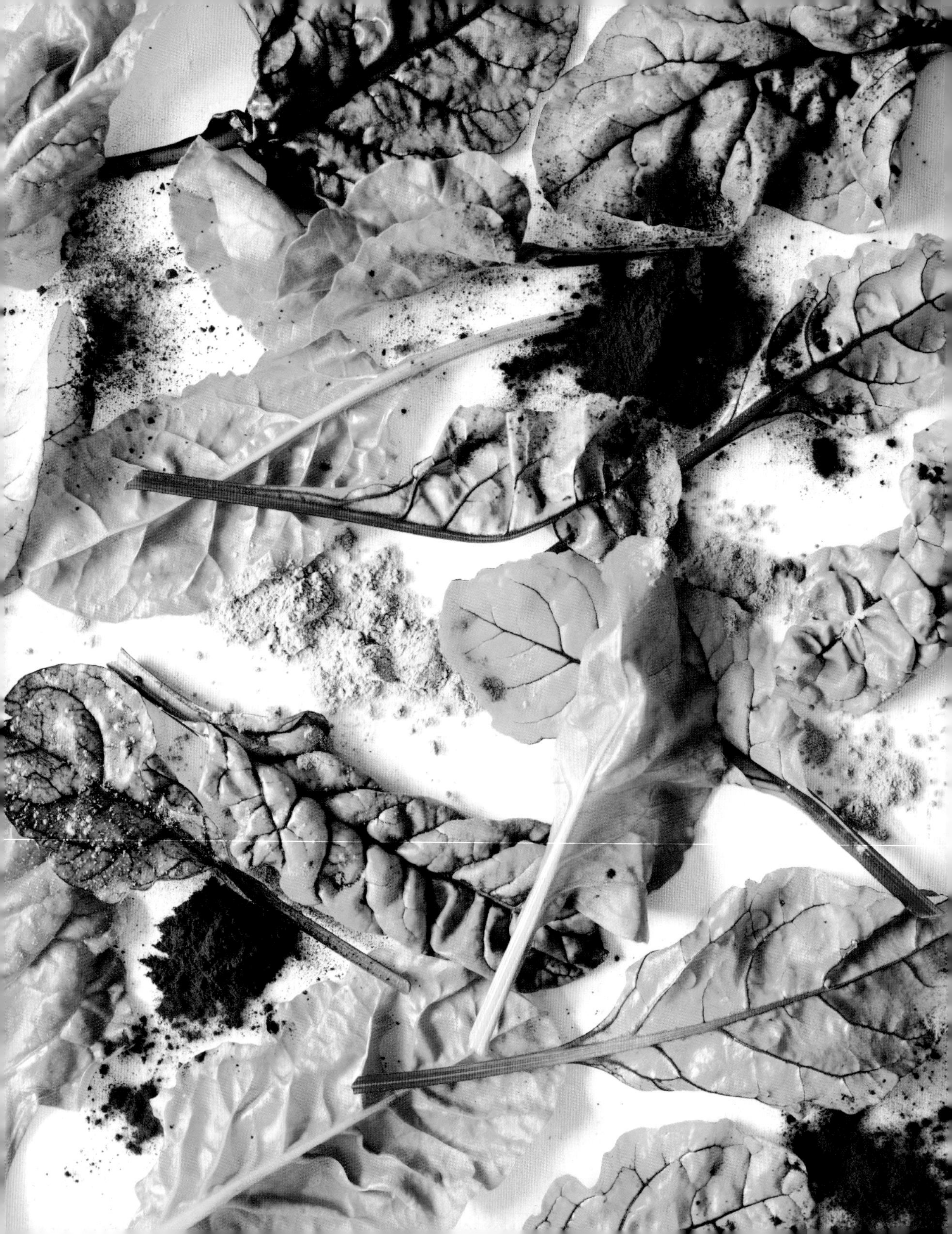

CHAPTER 3

YOUR SUPERCHARGED DIET MONTH

Power Your Way to a Slimmer, Healthier You

This 30-day *juice and smoothie* programme is designed for anyone wanting to lose more than half a stone (3.2kg/7lb) or who is seeking to make a longer-lasting commitment to their health. In the same way as the other plans, this programme will enable you to lose weight while simultaneously retraining your taste buds to enjoy healthy fruits and vegetables, making it easier to make long-lasting changes to your diet. The difference in this diet, apart from the time period, is that the 30-day programme incorporates an evening protein meal to provide sufficient nutrients to sustain a healthy weight loss through the entire 30 days while encouraging new healthy-eating patterns to ensure you have a permanently slim, trim and healthy body.

If you don't fancy a juice-only plan and are looking for a longer programme to get your body back into good health, then this 30-day juice and smoothie programme is for you.

Be prepared

It is particularly important to spend time preparing your body for this month-long programme before you start. The week before you intend to start your detox, gradually reduce your intake of coffee and tea, alcohol, processed and convenience foods and ready-meals, sugar and sweeteners, gluten, dairy and red meat except wild game. This will make it easier to follow the plan without having withdrawal symptoms from the foods you normally eat.

Drink 1–2 glasses of hot water with lemon and a slice of ginger each day to hydrate your body and kick-start your digestive system.

Two days before you are due to start on the plan, focus your meals on lean protein (poultry, fish, eggs and wild game) with plenty of vegetables and some fruit. Snack on nuts and seeds if you feel hungry. Include lots of water as well as nut milks, coconut water, coffee alternatives such as dandelion coffee, herbal teas and green tea.

Plan ahead by reading the recipes in this chapter and the sample plan below and decide which ingredients you need to buy in advance. Re-read The Supercharged Diet Basics starting on page 8 to make sure you are fully prepared. Buy a selection of fresh and frozen vegetables together with lean protein-rich foods (grass-fed lean red meat, wild game, chicken, fish, seafood, eggs, beans and pulses) to use to prepare your evening meal for this diet, as explained below.

How your plan works

Each morning, start the plan with a glass of hot water with the juice of ½ lemon and, if you wish, a slice of fresh ginger.

You will be drinking three juices and two smoothies spread throughout each day with a smoothie, Cinnamon Nut Milk or kefir at night. If you are particularly active, or your blood sugar levels dip during the day, you may wish to add a scoop of protein powder to one of the juices or swap one of the juices for another smoothie, which are generally high in calories and protein. A serving of juice or smoothie is approximately 400–500ml/14–17fl oz/1½–2 cups.

All the recipes are designed to serve one person, but the precise yield will vary depending on the size of the produce you use and the efficiency of your juicer.

As this is a longer programme, it is important that you include sufficient protein and some healthy fat each day. You will therefore also be eating an evening meal that contains protein and plenty of colourful vegetables.

During the programme I also recommend that you include plenty of smoothies that contain fermented drinks, such as kefir and kombucha, because these help to support optimal digestive function and immune health.

As well as the juices and smoothies, it is also important to drink plenty of liquids in the form of herbal teas, hot water with lemon or a slice of ginger, as well as water at room temperature. I recommend that you drink about 1l/35fl oz/ 4 cups water a day, which can be in the form of herbal teas. I also suggest you include a glass (measuring about 250ml/9fl oz/1 cup) of coconut water daily to keep your body hydrated.

Protein and blood sugar balance – essential for weight loss and energy

To keep your blood sugar level balanced and to sustain energy levels, drink a smoothie at lunch and dinner. Include a meal in the evening that is focused on protein and vegetables with some healthy fat. A glass of Cinnamon Nut Milk or coconut kefir will provide additional protein and healthy fat. You can sip this through the day, if you prefer, or drink it in the evening as a bedtime snack.

It is important to ensure you eat sufficient protein to help maintain healthy muscle mass as you lose weight. This will also ensure adequate energy levels through the day, avoiding cravings or energy dips.

Rest and exercise

During the 30-Day Plan you'll be ingesting fewer calories and macronutrients like protein, carbohydrates and fat than you usually would. Although you need to ensure you have sufficient rest, I nevertheless recommended you participate in light exercise regularly, such as walking, swimming, gentle yoga or Pilates.

Decide on your juice and smoothie selection

Look through the juices and smoothies in this, or any other, chapter in the book and select a variety each day. Use the following example day to guide you. If you do not have time to juice through the day, make up a double batch and store it in the fridge until required.

The Supercharged Diet Month daily plan

On waking hot water with lemon juice and ginger
Breakfast juice
Mid-morning juice
Lunch smoothie
Mid-afternoon juice
Dinner protein meal with vegetables, smoothie
Bedtime smoothie or Cinnamon Nut Milk or kefir
Throughout the day drink water, 1 glass coconut water, herbal teas, 1 glass Cinnamon Nut Milk or coconut kefir. Add 1–2 scoops of protein powder to one or two juices to balance your blood sugar level depending on your activity levels.

What to do after the plan

Congratulations on completing the Supercharged Diet Month! You should be feeling lighter, fresher and have a sense of renewed vitality. Moving forward, take a look at the recipes in the Supercharged Green for Life chapter that follows and try to include a juice or smoothie each day as a way to optimize your health in the long term. This could be as a healthy breakfast option or mid-morning/mid-afternoon snack, for example. Also, refer back to 'Continue to benefit from your diet plan' on page 10.

What if you need to lose more weight?

After the plan, if you wish to lose weight, limit your intake of starchy carbohydrates to one small portion a day (the equivalent of 125ml/4fl oz/½ cup in volume of cooked starchy vegetables) and focus on the following foods: pumpkin, butternut squash, beetroot, carrots or sweet potato, or the equivalent of 80ml/2½fl oz/⅓ cup in volume of cooked wholegrain rice or quinoa, or 2 oatcakes. Ditch all white refined carbohydrates and sweetened processed foods and drinks. Watch your intake of caffeine and alcohol too, as these can cause fluctuations in blood sugar levels, affecting energy and triggering cravings, which may result in weight gain.

Your evening meal

Keep your evening meal simple, but it is important to include a palm-sized portion of protein (about 120–150g/4¼–5½oz) such as fish, shellfish, lean grass-fed meat, wild game or poultry, or 2 eggs, 150g/5½oz/1 cup cooked beans or 150g/5½oz tofu. Add a plateful of colourful vegetables (about 2–3 handfuls), either lightly steamed or raw. You can steam, poach or bake your protein using coconut oil or olive oil. Add 1 teaspoon olive oil, omega blended oil or flaxseed oil to your meal if you are not baking (do not heat omega or flaxseed oils).

Your suggested Supercharged Diet Month sample week

Day 1

On waking Add the juice of ½ lemon to a 250ml/9fl oz/1 cup glass of hot water, with a thin slice of peeled root ginger, if you like
Breakfast Zesty Greens (page 84), plus 1 scoop of protein powder (optional)
Mid-morning Internal Balance (page 85)
Lunch Morning Shake (page 110)
Mid-afternoon Immune Kick (page 86)
Dinner Protein meal with vegetables, Chocolate Almond Recovery (page 90)
Bedtime Smoothie or Cinnamon Nut Milk (page 19), or 250ml/9fl oz/1 cup kefir
Throughout the day Drink 1l/35fl oz/4 cups water and a 250ml/9fl oz/1 cup glass of coconut water, plus herbal teas

Day 2

On waking Lemon and water, as Day 1
Breakfast Basil Green Cream (page 78), plus 1 scoop of protein powder (optional)
Mid-morning Beetroot Sensation (page 82)

Lunch Gingerbread Shake (page 88)
Mid-afternoon Joint Booster (page 82)
Dinner Protein meal with vegetables, Bedtime Blend (page 92)
Bedtime Smoothie or Cinnamon Nut Milk (page 19), or 250ml/9fl oz/1 cup kefir
Throughout the day Additional drinks, as Day 1

Day 3
On waking Lemon and water, as Day 1
Breakfast Leafy Energizer (page 85), plus 1 scoop of protein powder (optional)
Mid-morning Internal Balance (page 85)
Lunch Vitamin C Burst (page 93)
Mid-afternoon Zesty Greens (page 84)
Dinner Protein meal with vegetables, Iced Tea Cooler (page 90)
Bedtime Smoothie or Cinnamon Nut Milk (page 19), or 250ml/9fl oz/1 cup kefir
Throughout the day Additional drinks, as Day 1

Day 4
On waking Lemon and water, as Day 1
Breakfast Courgette Recovery (page 80), plus 1 scoop of protein powder (optional)
Mid-morning Beetroot Sensation (page 82)
Lunch Green Nourishment (page 98)
Mid-afternoon Lettuce Sparkler (page 84)
Dinner Protein meal with vegetables, Warm Elixir (page 96)
Bedtime Smoothie or Cinnamon Nut Milk (page 19), or 250ml/9fl oz/1 cup kefir
Throughout the day Additional drinks, as Day 1

Day 5
On waking Lemon and water, as Day 1
Breakfast Leafy Energizer (page 85), plus 1 scoop of protein powder (optional)
Mid-morning Immune Kick (page 86)
Lunch Probiotic Blast (page 100)
Mid-afternoon Joint Booster (page 82)
Dinner Protein meal with vegetables, Hormone Boost (page 102)
Bedtime Smoothie or Cinnamon Nut Milk (page 19), or 250ml/9fl oz/1 cup kefir
Throughout the day Additional drinks, as Day 1

Day 6
On waking Lemon and water, as Day 1
Breakfast Rich Green Immune Nectar (page 78), plus 1 scoop of protein powder (optional)
Mid-morning Zesty Greens (page 84)
Lunch Joint Support (page 94)
Mid-afternoon Basil Green Cream (page 78)
Dinner Protein meal with vegetables, Tropical Greens (page 92)
Bedtime Smoothie or Cinnamon Nut Milk (page 19), or 250ml/9fl oz/1 cup kefir
Throughout the day Additional drinks, as Day 1

Day 7
On waking Lemon and water, as Day 1
Breakfast Beetroot Sensation (page 82), plus 1 scoop of protein powder (optional)
Mid-morning Internal Balance (page 85)
Lunch Mint Chocolate Chip (page 104)
Mid-afternoon Zesty Greens (page 84)
Dinner Protein meal with vegetables, Kombucha Cleanse (page 101)
Bedtime Smoothie or Cinnamon Nut Milk (page 19), or 250ml/9fl oz/1 cup kefir
Throughout the day Additional drinks, as Day 1

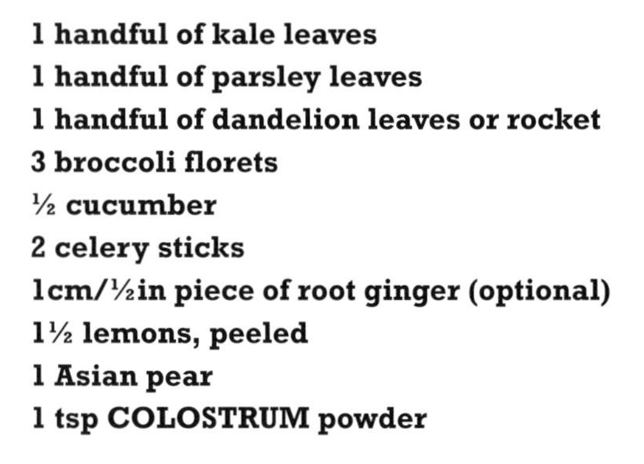

1 handful of kale leaves
1 handful of parsley leaves
1 handful of dandelion leaves or rocket
3 broccoli florets
½ cucumber
2 celery sticks
1cm/½in piece of root ginger (optional)
1½ lemons, peeled
1 Asian pear
1 tsp COLOSTRUM powder

Here is an invigorating green blend that is ideal for nourishing the blood and boosting energy. It's a great juice to perk up the body during the day. Antioxidant-rich dandelion acts as a mild laxative and diuretic – perfect for detoxing and weight loss. The juice also has alkalizing properties for promoting a strong immune system.

Put all the ingredients, except the colostrum, through an electric juicer. Stir in the colostrum and serve immediately.

Nutritional information per serving
Kcals 82 | **Protein** 5.2g
Carbohydrates 11.9g, of which sugars 11.3g
Fat 1.4g, of which saturates 0.2g

4 tbsp basil leaves
1 cucumber
1 lime, peeled
1 green apple
¼ tsp CHLORELLA powder
4 ice cubes

Think of this as a detox-friendly mojito. This juice is especially zesty and refreshing because it includes ice cubes and a whole lime. Including chlorella provides a burst of chlorophyll to promote cleansing, while its amino acids support energy and blood sugar balance – essential for a weight-loss programme.

Put all the ingredients, except the chlorella and ice, through an electric juicer. Transfer to a blender or food processor and add the chlorella and ice. Blend briefly to retain some texture. Serve immediately.

Nutritional information per serving
Kcals 77 | **Protein** 3.8g
Carbohydrates 13.3g, of which sugars 13g
Fat 0.6g, of which saturates 0g

Courgette Recovery

2 pears
2 small courgettes
½ lemon, peeled
1cm/½in piece of root ginger
5mm/¼in piece of TURMERIC ROOT or a pinch of ground TURMERIC
¼ tsp CAMU CAMU powder

Pears and courgettes combine to make a thirst-quenching juice lifted by the addition of ginger, turmeric and camu camu powder. It's a great drink to take after exercise, because alkaline vegetables, such as courgettes, will combat the build up of lactic acid, which can lead to post-exercise soreness. Choose this juice to refuel and replace lost fluids and electrolytes.

Put all the ingredients, except the ground turmeric, if using, and the camu camu, through an electric juicer. Stir in the camu camu and ground turmeric, and serve immediately.

Health Benefits

Courgettes are not only low in calories and carbohydrates but also rich in antioxidants, particularly carotenoids, which are important for skin and eye health. This juice is packed with vitamin C to support adrenal health and keep the body energized. It's a superb anti-inflammatory juice, thanks to the addition of ginger and turmeric. For a post-workout drink, add a scoop of protein powder to aid muscle recovery and repair.

G D S N SE V

Nutritional information per serving
Kcals 131 | **Protein** 8g
Carbohydrates 44.2g, of which sugars 15.5g
Fat 1.5g, of which saturates 0.4g

Joint Booster

1 pear
1 green apple
1 small handful of parsley leaves
4 celery sticks
1 handful of kale leaves
4 romaine lettuce leaves
1 lemon, peeled
1cm/½in piece of root ginger
¼ tsp MSM powder

Adding MSM powder to this fruity blend provides plenty of sulfur, which is a key nutrient for building connective tissue and maintaining healthy joints, skin and hair. Sulfur is also vital to support detoxification, making it valuable for weight loss. The juice is delicious as well as hydrating and alkalizing.

Put all the ingredients, except the MSM, through an electric juicer. Stir in the MSM and serve immediately.

Nutritional information per serving
Kcals 83 | **Protein** 3.8g
Carbohydrates 16g, of which sugars 15.3g
Fat 1.2g, of which saturates 0.1g

Beetroot Sensation

Pictured>

1 carrot
½ beetroot
1 orange, peeled
4 beet leaves
1 handful of coriander leaves
½ lemon, peeled
2 celery sticks
1cm/½in piece of root ginger
¼ tsp BLUEBERRY powder or AMLA BERRY powder

This juice is sweet yet nourishing. The phytonutrients in beetroot promote detoxification, assisting weight loss due to toxin reduction. They also cleanse the body and reduce water retention, which is often a cause of excess weight.

Put all the ingredients, except the blueberry, through an electric juicer. Stir in the blueberry and serve immediately.

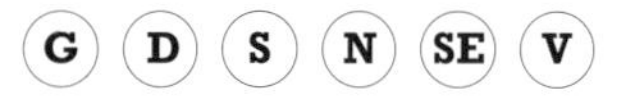

Nutritional information per serving
Kcals 115 | **Protein** 3.6g
Carbohydrates 22.3g, of which sugars 21.3g
Fat 1.3g, of which saturates 0.1g

Lettuce Sparkler

1 little gem lettuce
5cm/2in slice of skinned watermelon
½ lime, peeled
2 mint sprigs
¼ tsp BAOBAB powder
125ml/4fl oz/½ cup sparkling water
2–4 ice cubes, to taste

You can't beat a watermelon-based juice for the summer months! Low in calories, this lightly minty juice is hydrating after a night out or a hard workout, and it's packed with vitamin C to make it the perfect pick-me-up.

Put the lettuce, watermelon, lime and mint, through an electric juicer. Stir in the baobab, then add the sparkling water and ice cubes. Serve immediately.

Nutritional information per serving
Kcals 76 | **Protein** 2.5g
Carbohydrates 12.9g, of which sugars 12.9g
Fat 1.4g, of which saturates 0.3g

1 lemon, peeled
½ lime, peeled
1 handful of spinach leaves
4 celery sticks
½ cucumber
1 romaine lettuce
1 green apple
1 handful of kale leaves
¼ tsp MORINGA powder

Light and invigorating, this tangy juice will refresh you while it helps you shed the pounds. This cleansing combination contains electrolytes to balance the body's fluid levels and tackle bloating, helping you to get slim quickly.

Put all the ingredients, except the moringa, through an electric juicer. Stir in the moringa and serve immediately.

G D S N SE V

Nutritional information per serving
Kcals 81 | **Protein** 4.4g
Carbohydrates 12.4g, of which sugars 12.3g
Fat 1.4g, of which saturates 0.1g

Internal Balance

½ fennel bulb, chopped
1 handful of kale leaves
½ lemon, peeled
1 small handful of mint sprigs
1 cucumber
2 small green apples
1 tsp GLUTAMINE powder
½ tsp PROBIOTIC powder

A sweet-tasting blend, this juice contains glutamine, an essential amino acid to support muscle mass, which is essential on any weight-loss programme. It is also highly beneficial for the health of the gut lining. The blend also includes ingredients known to calm and soothe the digestive tract and support cleansing.

Put all the ingredients, except the glutamine and probiotic, through an electric juicer. Stir in the glutamine and probiotic, and serve the juice immediately.

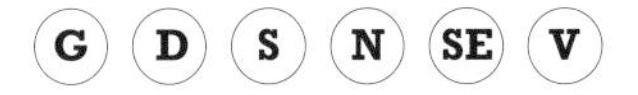

Nutritional information per serving
Kcals 120 | **Protein** 8g
Carbohydrates 21.3g, of which sugars 17.9g
Fat 1.2g, of which saturates 0.1g

Leafy Energizer

¼ pineapple, skin cut off
1 large handful of dandelion leaves or watercress
1 handful of kale leaves
1 lemon, peeled
½ cucumber
1 tsp CHIA SEEDS
¼ tsp GINSENG powder or 5 drops of GINSENG tincture

This pineapple-based juice contains ginseng, an adrenal adaptogenic herb that is ideal for boosting resilience and energy as you detox. Chia seeds are rich in omega-3 fats and soluble fibre to keep blood sugar levels balanced. Dandelion leaves are an ideal cleansing green to help reduce fluid retention.

Put all the ingredients, except the chia seeds and ginseng, through an electric juicer. Transfer to a blender or food processor and add the chia seeds and ginseng. Blend to combine, then serve immediately.

Nutritional information per serving
Kcals 121 | **Protein** 4.4g
Carbohydrates 19.7g, of which sugars 17.7g
Fat 2.8g, of which saturates 0.3g

Immune Kick

¼ tsp CHAGA MUSHROOM powder
1 handful of fresh or frozen raspberries
4 strawberries, hulled
¼ red chilli (optional), deseeded
½ lemon, peeled
1 large handful of spinach leaves
1cm/½in piece of root ginger
½ tsp GOJI BERRY powder

A comforting blend, this sweet-flavoured warm juice is ideal if you are seeking to lose weight during the winter months. It also packs a powerful immune punch. Rich in antioxidants and vitamin C, it is a good choice for perking up energy levels and invigorating the body.

Make a tea with the chaga by adding it to 150ml/5fl oz/scant ⅔ cup hot water. Leave to one side. Put the remaining ingredients, except the goji berry, through an electric juicer. Stir in the goji berry and chaga tea, and serve immediately.

Health Benefits

Chaga mushrooms are one of the most potent supercharged foods, tonics and energy boosters available and make a good purifying and detoxifying addition to this juice. Chaga is also known for its immune-enhancing properties and high levels of antioxidants, as well as possessing anti-viral properties. It is an amazing health and longevity tonic especially when combined with the antioxidant-rich berries in this juice.

G D S N SE V

Nutritional information per serving
Kcals 45 | **Protein** 2.7g
Carbohydrates 7.3g, of which sugars 6.7g
Fat 0.6g, of which saturates 0.2g

Gingerbread Shake

250ml/9fl oz/1 cup rooibos, or GREEN TEA or chai tea, warm
30g/1oz/scant ¼ cup VANILLA PROTEIN powder (optional)
1 handful of spinach leaves, chopped
¼ tsp ground ginger
a pinch of ground cardamom
1 tbsp almond nut butter
125ml/4fl oz/½ cup almond milk
2 tsp YACON syrup, or MANUKA or RAW HONEY
¼ tsp MORINGA powder
½ tsp ground cinnamon

Serve this tea- and protein-based shake warm for an uplifting drink. Yacon syrup won't disrupt your blood sugar and it acts as a prebiotic, providing food for your beneficial gut bacteria.

Put all the ingredients, except the cinnamon, into a blender or food processor and blend until smooth and creamy. Dust with the ground cinnamon and serve immediately.

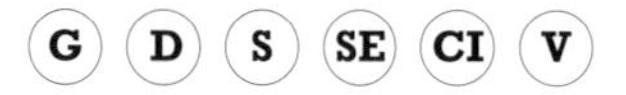

Nutritional information per serving
Kcals 158 | **Protein** 4.4g
Carbohydrates 21.8g, of which sugars 9.7g
Fat 9.2g, of which saturates 1.6g

Warming Detox Shake

4 broccoli florets
250ml/9fl oz/1 cup warm bone broth (marrow bone or chicken stock) (page 21)
¼ avocado, peeled and chopped
1–2 tsp white miso, to taste
¼ tsp CHLORELLA powder

Highly nutritious bone broth is the base for this warming drink, which is perfect for detox programmes during cooler months. Bone broth contains healing compounds such as collagen, proline, glycine and glutamine, making this smoothie perfect for digestive health, skin and joints.

Put the broccoli in a steamer over boiling water and cook for 5 minutes or until crisp-tender. Refresh under cold water. Put the broccoli into a blender or food processor and add the remaining ingredients. Blend until smooth and creamy. Serve immediately.

Nutritional information per serving
Kcals 89 | **Protein** 4.4g
Carbohydrates 3.4g, of which sugars 0.6g
Fat 6.2g, of which saturates 1.1g

Chocolate Almond Recovery

½ banana, peeled
1 tbsp RAW CACAO powder
30g/1oz/scant ¼ cup CHOCOLATE PROTEIN powder
1 small handful of cherries, pitted, frozen or fresh
2 large handfuls of kale leaves, chopped
½ tsp MACA powder
1 tbsp HEMP SEEDS
½ tsp GOJI BERRY powder
½ tsp vanilla extract
200ml/7fl oz/scant 1 cup almond milk

Eat more greens – the flavour is lost in this fruity–chocolate mix. The protein powder will give you energy, boost your metabolism and help you avoid cravings.

Chop the banana and put it into a freezer bag. Exclude all the air, then seal and freeze overnight or until solid. Put the banana into a blender or food processor and add the remaining ingredients. Blend until smooth and creamy. Serve immediately.

Nutritional information per serving
Kcals 379 | **Protein** 31.3g
Carbohydrates 43.5g, of which sugars 21.1g
Fat 8.8g, of which saturates 1.1g

Iced Tea Cooler

250ml/9fl oz/1 cup rooibos tea, or herbal tea or GREEN TEA, cooled
1 tsp CHIA SEEDS
1 tbsp lime juice
1 nectarine, peeled, pitted and chopped
1 handful of seedless green grapes
1 handful of greens, such as Swiss chard, spinach or lettuce leaves, chopped
¼ tsp WHEATGRASS powder
1 tbsp SEA BUCKTHORN juice (optional)
6 ice cubes

Cool down in the summer with this alkalizing smoothie. Wheatgrass is added for its beneficial minerals, to prompt detoxification and alkalize the body. For an extra glow, add a little sea buckthorn juice. It's rich in omega-7 fats – a natural skin moisturizer.

Put all the ingredients, except the ice, into a blender or food processor and blend until smooth and creamy. Add the ice and blend to create a slushy drink. Serve immediately.

Nutritional information per serving
Kcals 93 | **Protein** 3.4g
Carbohydrates 15.7g, of which sugars 13.3g
Fat 1.9g, of which saturates 0.2g

250ml/9fl oz/1 cup almond milk
1 small handful of pitted frozen cherries
2 tsp MONTMORENCY CHERRY concentrate
1 little gem lettuce, chopped
1 tbsp porridge oats, gluten-free if needed
½ banana, peeled and chopped
2 tsp ground FLAXSEED

Help yourself to this drink – and a good night's sleep. It includes ingredients that will boost levels of tryptophan, an amino acid the body converts to serotonin and melatonin – the sleep hormone. Quality sleep is essential for effective weight loss, so this blend helps to stabilize blood sugar and aids relaxation by boosting your sleep hormone.

Put all the ingredients into a blender or food processor and blend until smooth and creamy. Serve immediately.

Nutritional information per serving
Kcals 282 | **Protein** 6.7g
Carbohydrates 46.4g, of which sugars 23.4g
Fat 7.8g, of which saturates 0.8g

4 lychees, peeled and pitted
a small wedge of pineapple, skin cut off, chopped
2 handfuls of mixed greens, such as Swiss chard, spinach and kale leaves, chopped
1 tsp COCONUT OIL
1 tbsp coconut flakes
250ml/9fl oz/1 cup coconut water or water
¼ tsp WHEATGRASS powder or GREEN SUPERFOOD blend
4 ice cubes

Enjoy this exotic weight-loss blend to energize and alkalize your body. The addition of coconut oil boosts your energy levels and metabolism, while wheatgrass powder enhances detoxification and cleansing.

Put all the ingredients into a blender or food processor and blend until smooth and creamy. Serve immediately.

Nutritional information per serving
Kcals 215 | **Protein** 5g
Carbohydrates 24.8g, of which sugars 15.1g
Fat 10.5g, of which saturates 8g

½ papaya, peeled, deseeded and chopped
1 handful of spinach leaves, chopped
1 handful of kale leaves, chopped
1 tsp CHIA SEEDS
¼ tsp CAMU CAMU powder or ½ tsp BAOBAB powder
½ tsp PROBIOTIC powder
30g/1oz/scant ¼ cup VANILLA PROTEIN powder

Papaya makes a sweet base for this smoothie, but it is also nutrient rich. It is high in vitamin C and deeply energizing. It also contains the enzyme papain, which helps to promote digestive health and lower inflammation. Protein powder and chia seeds make the drink a suitable and satisfying breakfast option, stabilizing blood sugar throughout the morning and helping you to achieve effective weight loss.

Put all the ingredients into a blender or food processor and add 250ml/9fl oz/1 cup water. Blend until smooth and creamy. Serve immediately.

G **D** **S** **N** **CI** **V**

Nutritional information per serving
Kcals 196 | **Protein** 25.7g
Carbohydrates 13.7g, of which sugars 5.1g
Fat 4g, of which saturates 0.2g

1cm/½in piece of TURMERIC ROOT or ¼ tsp ground TURMERIC
1 carrot, chopped
1 handful of spinach leaves, chopped
½ mango, peeled and chopped
1 tbsp lime juice
30g/1oz/scant ¼ cup VANILLA PROTEIN powder
1 tbsp GLUTAMINE powder
4 ice cubes

If you enjoy taking exercise during your weight-loss programme, sip this blend after a workout. Packed with antioxidants, protein and carbohydrates, it will replenish glycogen stores and support muscle repair – fast. A dash of turmeric gives it a natural anti-inflammatory kick.

Put all the ingredients, except the ice cubes, into a blender or food processor and add 250ml/9fl oz/1 cup water. Blend until smooth and creamy, then add the ice and blend briefly to retain some texture. Serve the smoothie immediately.

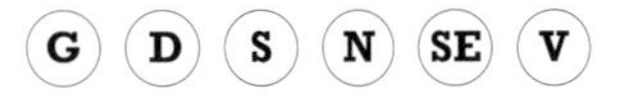

Nutritional information per serving
Kcals 239 | **Protein** 28.1g
Carbohydrates 27.4g, of which sugars 17.3g
Fat 2.9g, of which saturates 0.2g

5 broccoli florets
juice of ½ lime
1 celery stick, chopped
¼ cucumber, chopped
2 basil sprigs
1 green apple, cored and chopped
leaves from 2 mint sprigs
¼ avocado, peeled and chopped
1 tsp FLAXSEED OIL or OMEGA OIL blend
1 tbsp COLLAGEN powder
200ml/7fl oz/scant 1 cup coconut water or water

This creamy blend contains vitamin C to enhance the production of bone-essential collagen, and sulforaphane and indole-3-carbinol in the broccoli for joint support.

Put the broccoli in a steamer over boiling water and cook for 5 minutes or until crisp-tender. Refresh under cold water. Put the broccoli into a blender or food processor and add the remaining ingredients. Blend until smooth and creamy. Serve immediately.

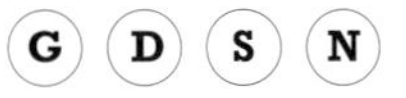

Nutritional information per serving
Kcals 234 | **Protein** 18.4g
Carbohydrates 18.1g, of which sugars 10.2g
Fat 9.7g, of which saturates 1.5g

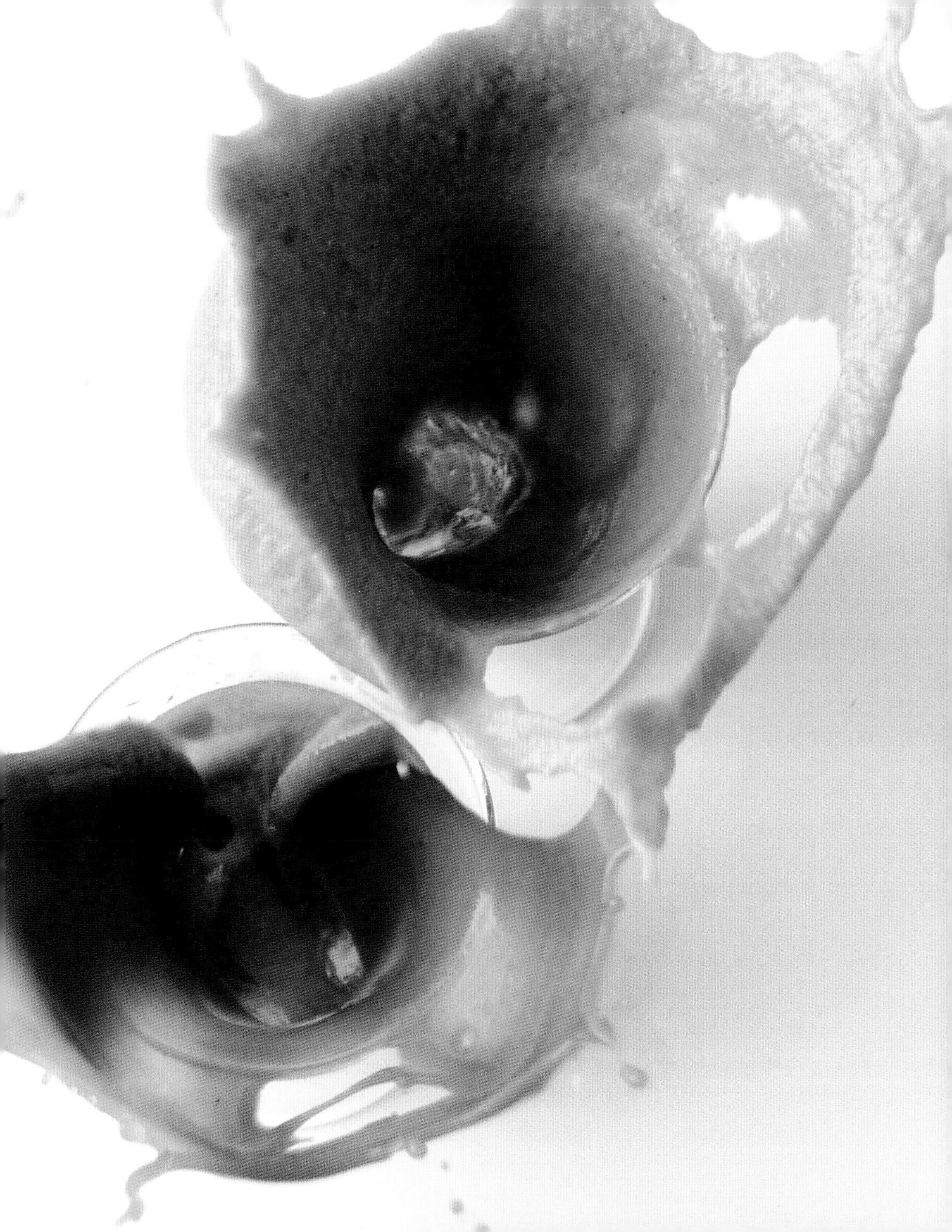

Warm Elixir

½ tsp CHAGA MUSHROOM powder
1 handful of spinach leaves, chopped
1 tbsp Brazil nut butter
1 tsp COCONUT OIL
¼ tsp ZEOLITE powder
1 tbsp RAW CACAO powder
1 tbsp LUCUMA powder
2 tsp BEE POLLEN
1 tsp MANUKA or RAW HONEY
1 large handful of pitted cherries
½ tsp vanilla extract
½ tsp ACAI BERRY powder

If you're looking for a comforting weight-loss drink, try this restorative chaga blend. Chaga is an amazing health and longevity tonic that will strengthen your body and restore vitality. Serve it warm to make a berry hot chocolate.

Make a tea with the chaga by adding it to 200ml/7fl oz/scant 1 cup hot water. Stir and leave to cool slightly. Put the remaining ingredients into a blender or food processor and add the tea. Blend until smooth and creamy. Serve immediately.

Health Benefits

Chaga is a medicinal mushroom that has anti-viral qualities and strong immune-enhancing properties, as well as high levels of antioxidants. Adding the Brazil nut butter provides good fat and selenium, which is important for a healthy thyroid and immune system. Zeolites are volcanic minerals known for their detoxification, anti-inflammatory and alkalizing properties. By lowering inflammation you can improve insulin function, which is essential for effective weight loss.

Nutritional information per serving
Kcals 308 | **Protein** 9.2g
Carbohydrates 38.6g, of which sugars 13.2g
Fat 12.4g, of which saturates 5g

Coconut Perfection

1 peach, pitted
6 strawberries, hulled
juice of ½ lime
1 handful of rocket leaves or spinach leaves, chopped
250ml/9fl oz/1 cup coconut milk
1 tsp vanilla extract
¼ tsp CAMU CAMU powder
1 tsp RAW CACAO NIBS

Creamy coconut milk gives this summer smoothie a lovely rich taste, and it's crammed with power-packed nutrients too. The addition of healthy fat will satisfy you and stabilize your blood sugar, making it easier to follow the plan and lose weight. The cacao nibs add a crunchy texture with a dose of magnesium to energize the body.

Put all the ingredients, except the cacao nibs, into a blender or food processor and blend until smooth and creamy. Stir in the cacao nibs and pulse to combine, leaving a little texture. Serve immediately.

Nutritional information per serving
Kcals 132 | **Protein** 4.7g
Carbohydrates 48.3g, of which sugars 19.7g
Fat 1.6g, of which saturates 0.8g

Green Nourishment

1 tbsp COLLAGEN powder
50g/1¾oz/⅓ cup cashew nuts
1 handful of kale leaves, chopped
1 tsp vanilla extract
¼ tsp CISSUS QUADRANGULARIS powder
¼ tsp MORINGA powder
¼ small pineapple, skin cut off, chopped

Nourish your body as you lose weight, with this creamy smoothie. Collagen is an essential protein for healthy bones and tissues, and it's great for supporting muscle mass as you lose weight. Traditionally, *Cissus quadrangularis* has been used to lower cortisol activity: high cortisol can lead to weight gain and more tummy fat.

Put all the ingredients into a blender or food processor and add 250ml/9fl oz/1 cup water. Blend until smooth and creamy. Serve the smoothie immediately.

Nutritional information per serving
Kcals 416 | **Protein** 25.7g
Carbohydrates 23.1g, of which sugars 17g
Fat 24.9g, of which saturates 4.8g

250ml/9fl oz/1 cup hemp milk or coconut milk
1 banana, peeled and chopped
¼ avocado, peeled and chopped
¼ tsp SPIRULINA powder
30g/1oz/scant ¼ cup HEMP PROTEIN powder
¼ tsp BAOBAB powder
1 handful of spinach leaves, chopped
a pinch of stevia or xylitol, to taste (optional)

If you like to work out, try this protein-packed elixir to take afterwards. It is rich in healthy fats, potassium and magnesium, to hydrate the body, and antioxidants to aid recovery. Adding protein to the mix boosts your muscle mass and metabolism, which is essential for effectively sustaining weight loss.

Put all the ingredients, except the stevia, into a blender or food processor and blend until smooth and creamy. Sweeten with stevia, if needed. Stir and serve immediately.

Nutritional information per serving
Kcals 351 | **Protein** 25.9g
Carbohydrates 33.4g, of which sugars 29g
Fat 12.1g, of which saturates 1.2g

½ small banana, peeled
250ml/9fl oz/1 cup MILK KEFIR or COCONUT KEFIR (page 20)
1 tbsp GOJI BERRIES
¼ tsp ACAI BERRY powder
1 handful of fresh or frozen mixed berries
1 large handful of spinach leaves, chopped
½ tsp PROBIOTIC powder

This gut-friendly, immune-supporting creamy drink is a wonderful smoothie for balancing blood sugar levels, making it easier to lose weight. Packed with beneficial bacteria, kefir is a health-promoting drink used for centuries to support overall health and longevity.

Chop the banana and put it into a freezer bag. Exclude all the air, then seal and freeze overnight or until solid. Put the banana into a blender or food processor and add the remaining ingredients. Blend until smooth and creamy. Serve immediately.

Nutritional information per serving
Kcals 288 | **Protein** 10.5g
Carbohydrates 36.8g, of which sugars 34g
Fat 11g, of which saturates 6.3g

Kombucha Cleanse

250ml/9fl oz/1 cup KOMBUCHA (page 21)
1 kiwi fruit, peeled and chopped
1 handful of parsley leaves
1 pear, cored and chopped
juice of ½ lemon
¼ cucumber, chopped
4 ice cubes

Super-light with cucumber, kiwi, pear and parsley, this refreshing smoothie has kombucha fermented tea as its base. Kombucha contains a wealth of probiotics to support digestive health and to detoxify and strengthen the immune system, making it a great cleansing juice for weight loss.

Put all the ingredients into a blender or food processor and blend until smooth and creamy. Serve immediately.

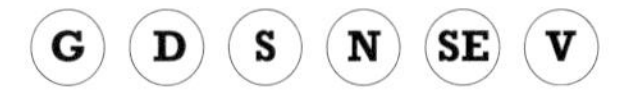

Nutritional information per serving
Kcals 81 | **Protein** 1.6g
Carbohydrates 16.7g, of which sugars 9.2g
Fat 0.5g, of which saturates 0g

Green Kefir

1 kiwi fruit, peeled and chopped
250ml/9fl oz/1 cup WATER KEFIR (page 20) or KOMBUCHA (page 21) or coconut water
½ cucumber, chopped
1 small handful of spring greens, spinach or kale, chopped
2 mint leaves
1 small sliver of peeled root ginger (optional)
4 ice cubes

Probiotics are abundant in water kefir, which makes a revitalizing base for a fruity and minty cooler, fresh with greens and cucumber. Low in calories and hydrating, this blend is super-cleansing to support your weight loss.

Put all the ingredients, except the ice, into a blender or food processor and blend until smooth and creamy. Add the ice and blend to create a slushy drink. Serve immediately.

Nutritional information per serving
Kcals 85 | **Protein** 2.6g
Carbohydrates 16g, of which sugars 8.3g
Fat 0.7g, of which saturates 0g

Hormone Boost

1 small banana, peeled
1 handful of kale leaves, chopped
½ tsp ROYAL JELLY POWDER or BEE POLLEN
1 tbsp RAW CACAO powder
1 tbsp RAW CACAO BUTTER, melted, or 1 tsp COCONUT OIL (optional)
1 tsp shelled HEMP SEEDS
½ tsp MACA powder
2 tsp LUCUMA powder
½ tsp vanilla extract
¼ tsp MUCUNA PRURIENS powder
1 tsp pumpkin seeds
250ml/9fl oz/1 cup almond or coconut milk
a pinch of stevia or xylitol, to taste

Cacao powder, cacao butter and almond milk make a rich-tasting smoothie designed to stabilize blood sugar and keep you feeling fuller for longer. This will help to reduce cravings, making it easier to stick to the weight-loss plan.

Chop the banana and put it into a freezer bag. Exclude all the air, then seal and freeze overnight or until solid. Put the banana into a blender or food processor and add the remaining ingredients. Blend until smooth and creamy. Serve immediately.

Health Benefits

Mucuna pruriens is an exceptionally potent mood-enhancing and libido-stimulating food, containing the amino acid, L-dopa, from which your body makes dopamine, a powerful neurotransmitter that boosts your mood, alertness and libido. Because dopamine is a stimulating neurotransmitter, it will help you stick to your diet goals and feel motivated.

G D S CI

Nutritional information per serving
Kcals 378 | **Protein** 9.5g
Carbohydrates 48.1g, of which sugars 17.4g
Fat 16.2g, of which saturates 5.7g

seeds of ½ pomegranate
1 tsp POMEGRANATE powder
1 tsp ACAI BERRY powder or MAQUI BERRY powder
6 strawberries, hulled
1 tbsp GOJI BERRIES
1 large handful of spring greens, chopped

Power-packed, anti-inflammatory and antioxidant-rich, this is a vitality-boosting, vitamin- and mineral-rich shake. By lowering inflammation you can enhance your metabolic function, thereby improving your ability to burn energy and avoid weight gain. It also provides phytoestrogens, which can be helpful for balancing the female hormones.

Put all the ingredients into a blender or food processor and add 250ml/9fl oz/1 cup water. Blend until smooth and creamy. Serve the smoothie immediately.

Nutritional information per serving
Kcals 100 | **Protein** 2.3g
Carbohydrates 20.6g, of which sugars 17.8g
Fat 1.2g, of which saturates 0g

Pictured>

30g/1oz/scant ¼ cup VANILLA or PLAIN PROTEIN powder
1 handful of kale leaves, chopped
1 tsp GREEN SUPERFOOD blend
6 mint leaves
125ml/4fl oz/½ cup water or coconut water
¼ avocado, peeled and chopped
150ml/5fl oz/scant ⅔ cup almond milk
1 tsp xylitol or a few drops of stevia, to taste
1 tbsp RAW CACAO NIBS
4 ice cubes

This tasty milkshake will satisfy you as well as boosting your weight loss, thanks to its protein content. Take this as a quick breakfast or a healthy snack to restore flagging energy levels.

Put all the ingredients, except the cacao nibs and ice, into a blender or food processor and blend until smooth and creamy. Add the cacao nibs and ice, and pulse to combine, keeping some texture.

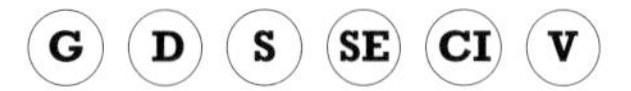

Nutritional information per serving
Kcals 367 | **Protein** 28.1g
Carbohydrates 31.8g, of which sugars 4.8g
Fat 16.7g, of which saturates 4.8g

Stress Buster

1 large handful of cos or romaine lettuce leaves, chopped
1 tbsp almond nut butter
¼ tsp ASHWAGANDHA powder
½ tsp MACA powder
1 large handful of frozen mixed berries
1 tsp COCONUT OIL or MCT OIL
1 tsp BEE POLLEN (optional)
250ml/9fl oz/1 cup MILK KEFIR (page 20), or coconut milk or almond milk
a pinch of stevia or xylitol, to taste (optional)

The combination of foods in this creamy shake is packed with elements that support adrenal function and restore vitality. Excess cortisol, our stress hormone, interferes with blood sugar levels and increases appetite, making us more likely to overeat. Cortisol also results in more tummy fat and can reduce our muscle mass. Use MCT (medium-chain triglyceride) oil, if you can, to provide an instant energy lift.

Put all the ingredients into a blender or food processor and blend until smooth and creamy. Serve immediately.

Health Benefits

Ashwagandha root is one of the most vital herbs for healing in the Ayurvedic healing system. It is a well-known adaptogenic herb, which helps to balance our levels of stress hormones and improve the functioning of the thyroid gland, which is essential for a healthy metabolism and for supporting weight loss.

G S SE CI

Nutritional information per serving
Kcals 262 | **Protein** 15.9g
Carbohydrates 18.4g, of which sugars 3.6g
Fat 13.2g, of which saturates 4.2g

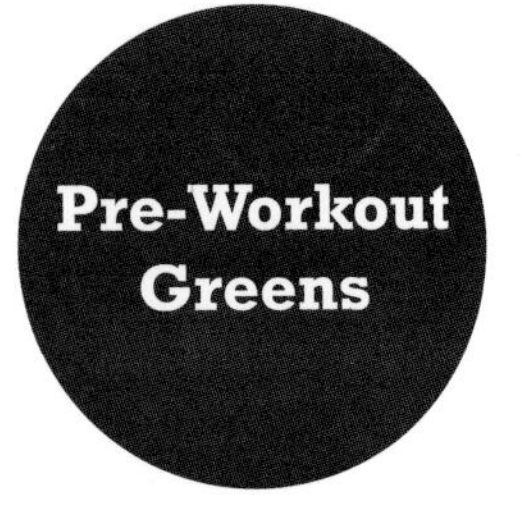

1 small banana, peeled
1 handful of kale leaves, chopped
1 handful of spinach leaves, chopped
¼ avocado, peeled and chopped
1 tsp CHIA SEEDS
juice of ½ lime
½ tsp coconut oil
¼ tsp MATCHA GREEN TEA powder
250ml/9fl oz/1 cup coconut water

Experience the fat-boosting and performance benefits of matcha by making this delicious blend. It's an ideal pre-workout drink designed to hydrate and energize your body for optimum performance. Green tea increases fat-burning and enables you to work out harder for longer.

Chop the banana and put it into a freezer bag. Exclude all the air, then seal and freeze overnight or until solid. Put the banana into a blender or food processor and add the remaining ingredients. Blend until smooth and creamy. Serve immediately.

Nutritional information per serving
Kcals 220 | **Protein** 6.1g
Carbohydrates 29.5g, of which sugars 16.8g
Fat 8.9g, of which saturates 2.6g

1cm/½in piece of root ginger, peeled and chopped
½ mango, peeled and chopped
1 carrot, chopped
250ml/9fl oz/1 cup COCONUT KEFIR (page 20) or coconut milk
1 tsp COCONUT OIL
1 tbsp LUCUMA powder
a pinch of ground TURMERIC

This fabulous anti-inflammatory shake is creamy with a sweet edge from mango and lucuma powder. It's a superb blend to boost energy and metabolism as you detox. It is also rich in carotenoids to support the immune system.

Put all the ingredients into a blender or food processor and blend until smooth and creamy. Serve immediately.

Nutritional information per serving
Kcals 283 | **Protein** 13.4g
Carbohydrates 42.5g, of which sugars 14.4g
Fat 5.5g, of which saturates 2.8g

1 handful of fresh or frozen blueberries
2 tbsp pomegranate seeds
1 tbsp GOJI BERRIES
½ tsp MAQUI BERRY powder or SUPERBERRY powder
1 tsp HEMPSEED OIL or FLAXSEED OIL (optional)
¼ tsp BAOBAB powder
1 large handful of spinach leaves, chopped
¼ tsp ASTRAGALUS powder
1 tbsp cashew nuts
150ml/5fl oz/scant ⅔ cup almond milk
150ml/5fl oz/scant ⅔ cup pomegranate juice

This antioxidant-rich blend is ideal for sustaining energy through the day, relieving fatigue and reducing cravings. Astralagus strengthens the immune system and boosts energy.

Put all the ingredients into a blender or food processor and blend until smooth and creamy. Serve immediately.

Nutritional information per serving
Kcals 330 | **Protein** 5.5g
Carbohydrates 45.5g, of which sugars 30g
Fat 13.7g, of which saturates 1.8g

1 small banana, peeled
100ml/3½fl oz/generous ⅓ cup black coffee, or decaffeinated coffee, cooled
1 tsp sunflower seed butter or tahini
½ tsp MACA powder
1 tbsp RAW CACAO powder
1 tbsp LUCUMA powder
½ romaine lettuce, chopped
250ml/9fl oz/1 cup almond milk
1 tsp CHIA SEEDS
1 tsp YACON syrup or coconut syrup
1 tsp RAW CACAO NIBS

Almond milk makes a rich base for this nutritious weight-loss pick-me-up, with maca to boost your energy and resilience.

Chop the banana and put it into a freezer bag. Exclude all the air, then seal and freeze overnight or until solid. Put the banana into a blender or food processor and add the remaining ingredients, except the cacao nibs, and process until creamy. Pour into a glass and top with the nibs. Serve the smoothie immediately.

Nutritional information per serving
Kcals 342 | **Protein** 8.4g
Carbohydrates 60g, of which sugars 24.7g
Fat 8.6g, of which saturates 1.5g

1 orange, peeled and chopped
½ tsp MACA powder
½ tsp GOJI BERRY powder
½ tsp BEE POLLEN
¼ mango, peeled and chopped
1 handful of spring greens, or Swiss chard, spinach or kale leaves, chopped
30g/1oz/scant ¼ cup VANILLA PROTEIN powder
250ml/9fl oz/1 cup GREEN TEA

If you usually have a glass of orange juice at breakfast, supercharge it with this fabulous fat-busting smoothie. Adding a scoop of protein powder will help to boost your metabolism and stabilize your blood sugar level, as well as keeping you energized throughout the morning.

Put all the ingredients into a blender or food processor and blend until smooth and creamy. Serve immediately.

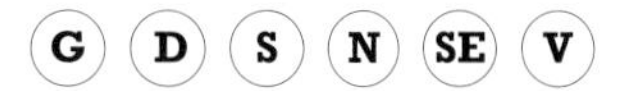

Nutritional information per serving
Kcals 215 | **Protein** 26.3g
Carbohydrates 21.7g, of which sugars 15.5g
Fat 2.7g, of which saturates 0.1g

250ml/9fl oz/1 cup black coffee, cooled
1 handful of spinach leaves, chopped
2 tsp RAW CACAO powder
2 pitted soft dried dates, chopped
½ tsp vanilla extract
4 ice cubes
125ml/4fl oz/½ cup almond milk
a pinch of stevia or xylitol, to taste (optional)

If you love your morning cuppa, try blending up this delicious combination. Coffee is known to kick-start the metabolism, lift energy and boost weight loss. Adding a little raw cacao gives this shake a subtle chocolate flavour and boosts your intake of energizing magnesium too.

Put all the ingredients, except the stevia, into a blender or food processor and blend until smooth and creamy. Sweeten with stevia, if needed. Stir and serve immediately.

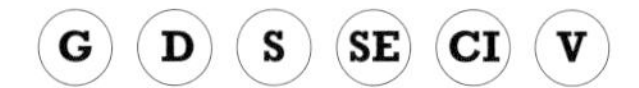

Nutritional information per serving
Kcals 92 | **Protein** 2.6g
Carbohydrates 15.5g, of which sugars 5.5g
Fat 2.1g, of which saturates 0.4g

Red Pepper Savoury Blend

1 handful of kale or spinach leaves, chopped
1 red pepper, deseeded and chopped
4 tomatoes, chopped
juice of ½ lemon
2 tsp NUTRITIONAL YEAST FLAKES
a pinch of dried chilli flakes
2 tsp shelled HEMP SEEDS
a pinch of NORI flakes

This is like a raw soup in a glass, with all its goodness. It's a great option for lunch and is incredibly satisfying. The addition of nori flakes, chilli and nutritional yeast flakes keeps the body energized by supporting metabolism. It's also fabulous for healthy skin – hydrating and rich in skin-friendly vitamin A.

Put all the ingredients into a blender or food processor and add 100ml/3½ fl oz/generous ⅓ cup water. Blend until smooth and creamy, adding more water if needed. Serve the smoothie immediately.

Nutritional information per serving
Kcals 174 | **Protein** 11.4g
Carbohydrates 17.8g, of which sugars 14.2g
Fat 6.3g, of which saturates 0.7g

Creamy Cucumber

Pictured>

½ cucumber, chopped
1 handful of spinach leaves, chopped
1 tbsp lime juice
¼ avocado, peeled and chopped
6 strawberries, hulled
¼ tsp GREEN SUPERFOOD blend or WHEATGRASS powder
200ml/7fl oz/scant 1 cup almond milk
leaves from 1 mint sprig
1 pitted fresh date or a few drops of stevia (optional)

Take this hydrating summer smoothie to refresh flagging energy levels. The green superfood powder contains antioxidants and chlorophyll to support detoxification, while the avocado provides healthy fats to keep away those cravings. Add a fresh date or a little stevia if you like it to be a bit sweeter.

Put all the ingredients into a blender or food processor and blend until smooth and creamy. Serve immediately.

Nutritional information per serving
Kcals 141 | **Protein** 3.4g
Carbohydrates 14.5g, of which sugars 5.6g
Fat 7.3g, of which saturates 1g

CHAPTER 4

YOUR SUPERCHARGED GREEN FOR LIFE

Daily Ways to Boost Your Health

Whether you have followed one of the programmes in this book or you simply wish to optimize your health and vitality, taking one or two of my supercharged juices or smoothies daily is a simple and effective way to enhance your health and promote healthy ageing. You can choose any of the drinks in this book, but the recipes in this section focus on weight maintenance and additional health benefits.

Look at food with fresh eyes

To reap the most benefits from the drinks, however, it's important that you pay attention to your diet and lifestyle as a whole. There is no point in adding a supercharged juice or smoothie to your diet if the rest of your food choices are devoid of nutrients or centred on processed foods, sugars and refined carbohydrates. Such foods are empty calories and will not contribute to your health or vitality – and they may result in weight gain too. Some foods or drinks that are regularly consumed contain anti-nutrients; that is, they can either block the absorption of key vitamins and minerals or deplete the body of certain nutrients. Alcohol, for example, will deplete the body of B vitamins; tannins in tea can interfere with the absorption of calcium and iron; and phytates found in many grains can also interfere with absorption of minerals such as zinc, calcium and iron. It is therefore worth thinking about reducing the amount of alcohol, tea and grains that you consume.

You will find guidance on eating healthily in the 'Continue to benefit from your diet plan' information on page 10.

Balance your body for the best of health

One of the benefits of taking my supercharged drinks is that they are alkalizing. If you want to age well, alkaline foods should be a key feature in your diet. A predominantly acid-forming diet (one that is very high in grains, beans and pulses, sugar, alcohol, coffee, meat, fish and eggs) increases the body's requirement for alkalizing minerals (such as calcium, magnesium and potassium) and can put an unnecessary strain on the vital organs, particularly the liver and kidneys. To keep your body in a healthy acid–alkaline balance, you need to consume plenty of alkaline-forming foods – vegetables and fruits – daily in addition to healthy protein-rich foods such as meat, fish and eggs.

One of the most effective ways to do this is to include the delicious supercharged drinks in this book daily as a snack, or to replace a meal, to take pre-workout or as a post-workout pick-me-up. When you drink a green juice or smoothie, you will be consuming a much larger amount of vegetables than you would normally eat. Plus, you will have a nutrient boost from the supercharged ingredients. This concentrated dose of easy-to-digest nutrients and antioxidants will support a healthy, more vital and leaner body for life.

Supercharged juices and smoothies are suitable for most people. Even those who suffer with irritable bowel syndrome, Crohn's disease or other types of gastrointestinal problems can usually tolerate these drinks, whereas they might not be able to eat a great deal of raw food.

If you suffer with blood sugar imbalances, I suggest that you focus on those smoothies that contain more fibre as well as healthy fats and proteins to stabilize your blood sugar levels.

Green juices and smoothies are also ideal ways to hydrate your body, alongside drinking plenty of fluids such as water or herbal teas. Adequate hydration is essential to promote energy levels and clear thinking as well as contributing to healthy, glowing skin. Drinking too little, on the other hand, can make you feel tired, lead to toxic build-up and cause constipation as well as drying out the skin and joints.

Avoid falling into the convenience trap

I recommend that your diet is focused on natural whole foods with plenty of colour on your plate. Keep processed foods to a minimum. Avoid ready-meals, takeaways, microwave meals, foods containing artificial preservatives and chemicals, trans-fats and high-fructose corn syrup.

Base your diet on fresh, colourful vegetables, herbs, sea vegetables, spices, nuts and seeds, fermented foods, beans and pulses (if you are vegan or vegetarian) and low-fructose fruits such as citrus and berries. If you eat animal products, aim for organic, free-range eggs and poultry, wild-caught fish, wild game and naturally reared animals. Take fermented foods daily, such as kefir or kombucha, which are used in drinks throughout this book. Or eat yogurt, raw sauerkraut, kimchi, pickled vegetables or miso.

Eat mindfully

When you consume food and your supercharged drinks, do so consciously. Take your time over your meals. Rather than eating on the run, sit at a table and eat slowly and mindfully. In the same way, don't gulp your drinks, but savour them slowly and gratefully. Doing so will promote healthy digestion, it will slow down the release of sugar into the bloodstream and will help to keep your blood sugar levels stable. Eating slowly and mindfully will also make you less likely to overeat.

Remember that although these drinks are incredibly nutrient dense, for long-term health they should complement, and not replace, a varied diet based on natural whole foods.

Find your health booster

I also recommend that you try a variety of the recipes from the other chapters in this book. Use the Quick Look section on pages 150–157 to select blends that suit your specific needs; for example, there may be times when you feel you need more energy or protein, especially if you enjoy exercise. Many of the drinks are perfect as a pre- or post-workout snack. Alternatively, there may be times when you are aiming to support specific body systems; for example, brain health, stress, metabolism, skin, hair, bone health or joints. Other drinks are designed for anti-ageing and longevity. If you experience ongoing inflammation or pain, one or two daily drinks can be beneficial – all the juices and smoothies contain key nutrients and ingredients known to lower inflammation in the body naturally.

The combination of fresh and wholesome ingredients in these blends works synergistically to nourish and enhance your beauty, brain, body and spirit from within. Not only are they nourishing but they also have the power to transform your health at the deepest level. When you include these juices and smoothies daily, you'll notice a shift in your health and you'll feel inspired to adopt a new way of living and eating to nourish your body and bring with it long-term wellness and vitality.

½ beetroot
1 carrot
1 grapefruit, peeled
1 celery stick
2 chard leaves or 1 handful of mixed greens, such as Swiss chard, spinach and kale leaves
½ tsp CAMU CAMU powder

Mineral-packed root veg make the base of this delicious, immune-boosting juice. Grapefruit is a low-calorie fruit known for its ability to boost weight loss and enhance cleansing. The camu camu berry is one of the world's most abundant sources of vitamin C – as much as 60 times more per serving than an orange. It also supplies potassium, calcium and beta-carotene.

Put all the ingredients, except the camu camu, through an electric juicer. Stir in the camu camu and serve immediately.

Nutritional information per serving
Kcals 133 | **Protein** 5g
Carbohydrates 49.8g, of which sugars 20.4g
Fat 0.6g, of which saturates 0.1g

1 pear
1 cucumber
2 celery sticks
½ lemon, peeled
1 large handful of spinach leaves
½ tsp WHEATGRASS powder or GREEN SUPERFOOD blend
2 drops of ZEOLITE liquid (optional)

Nutritious wheatgrass powder makes this juice into a powerful chlorophyll booster for you to use to cleanse, recharge and refresh your body. For an additional detox shot, add some liquid zeolite.

Put all the ingredients, except the wheatgrass and zeolite, if using, through an electric juicer. Stir in the wheatgrass and zeolite, and serve immediately.

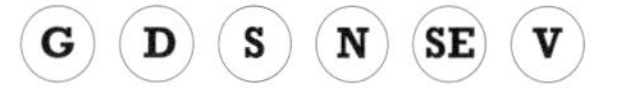

Nutritional information per serving
Kcals 88 | **Protein** 4.4g
Carbohydrates 14g, of which sugars 12.9g
Fat 0.8g, of which saturates 0.1g

2 carrots
2 Swiss chard leaves or 1 handful of spinach leaves
1 lime, peeled
1 green apple
1cm/½in piece of root ginger
½ tsp MACA powder
150ml/5fl oz/scant ⅔ cup coconut water

A healthy thyroid and hormones are important key players in reaching your weight-loss or general health goals. Maca powder works to balance hormones and improve the functioning of the adrenals and thyroid, thereby naturally supporting weight loss. This carrot, ginger and chard juice is packed with beta-carotene, making it ideal for skin health and immune function.

Put all the ingredients, except the maca and coconut water, through an electric juicer. Transfer to a blender or food processor and add the maca and coconut water. Blend to combine and serve immediately.

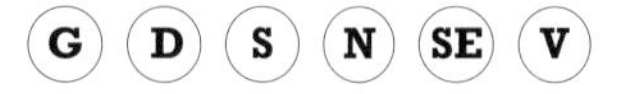

Nutritional information per serving
Kcals 178 | **Protein** 4.1g
Carbohydrates 37g, of which sugars 29g
Fat 1.4g, of which saturates 0.3g

Pictured>

¼ small pineapple, skin cut off
1 cucumber
½ lemon, peeled
1cm/½in piece of root ginger
4 broccoli florets
1 large handful of spinach leaves
1 tsp OMEGA OIL blend or FLAXSEED OIL
¼ tsp MSM powder

Look fabulous as you keep slim and toned. This vitamin- and mineral-rich blend will transform dull hair into luscious locks. Broccoli contains vitamins A and C to produce sebum and keep your hair moisturized. Spinach provides the healthy-hair essentials of iron and folate, and omega oils keep your skin and hair in good condition.

Put all the ingredients, except the oil and MSM, through an electric juicer. Stir in the oil and MSM, and serve immediately.

Nutritional information per serving
Kcals 159 | **Protein** 6.7g
Carbohydrates 22g, of which sugars 21g
Fat 5g, of which saturates 0.5g

Green-Ade

1 lemon, peeled
1 cos or romaine lettuce
1cm/½in piece of root ginger
1 celery stick
1cm/½in piece of TURMERIC ROOT or ¼ tsp ground TURMERIC
½ tsp BAOBAB powder or CAMU CAMU powder
1 tsp YACON syrup or maple syrup
200ml/7fl oz/scant 1 cup coconut water

This super-refreshing, low-cal, green 'lemonade' contains anti-inflammatory spices – ginger and turmeric – and makes an ideal drink for maintaining a healthy weight. It's a wonderfully hydrating drink for the warm weather, and you could also blend in ice cubes for an icy cooler when the temperature is really high.

Put the lemon, lettuce, ginger, celery and turmeric root (but not the ground turmeric, if using) through an electric juicer. Stir in the ground turmeric, the baobab, yacon syrup and coconut water, and serve immediately.

Health Benefits

Packed with vitamin C, baobab is invigorating and adds a delicious citrus tang to drinks. It's ideal for supporting immune health and protecting the body from free-radical damage. Vitamin C is required for the healthy production of collagen, making it valuable for fresh-looking, glowing skin.

G D S N SE V

Nutritional information per serving
Kcals 118 | **Protein** 5.5g
Carbohydrates 21.2g, of which sugars 11.3g
Fat 2.8g, of which saturates 0.4g

Digestion Soother

1 lime, peeled
1 green apple
½ cucumber
1 small handful of parsley
1 handful of spinach leaves
1cm/½in piece of root ginger
½ tsp PROBIOTIC powder

Apple is great for digestive support because it is rich in pectin, a soluble fibre that aids digestion and improves bowel function. By keeping the fruit to a minimum, this is an excellent low-sugar, cleansing juice. The addition of probiotics supports overall digestion and immune function.

Put all the ingredients, except the probiotic, through an electric juicer. Stir in the probiotic and serve immediately.

Nutritional information per serving
Kcals 62 | **Protein** 2.8g
Carbohydrates 10.8g, of which sugars 10.8g
Fat 0.6g, of which saturates 0g

Watercress Punch

1 handful of watercress
1 lime, peeled
2 mint sprigs
2 green apples
½ tsp NONI powder or BAOBAB powder

This punchy, bright-green juice is low in calories and deeply cleansing. It is packed with iron and B vitamins to boost energy. It also contains noni powder, which is rich in amino acids and immunity-enhancing polysaccharides. Noni is also a useful source of vitamin C, dietary fibre, iron and potassium.

Put all the ingredients, except the noni, through an electric juicer. Stir in the noni and serve immediately.

Nutritional information per serving
Kcals 56 | **Protein** 1.4g
Carbohydrates 11.4g, of which sugars 11.4g
Fat 0.5g, of which saturates 0.1g

Pure Greens

1 lemon, peeled
1 courgette
1 handful of spinach leaves
½ fennel bulb
1 cucumber
½ tsp BAOBAB powder

If you're a fan of very low-sugar green juices, try this blend, packed with leafy goodness. The spinach contains B vitamins and iron to energize the body. Courgette and cucumber rehydrate the body and replace lost electrolytes, ideal for tackling any bloating or water retention. Baobab gives the juice a vitamin-C burst plus fibre to provide an energy boost.

Put all the ingredients, except the baobab, through an electric juicer. Stir in the baobab and serve immediately.

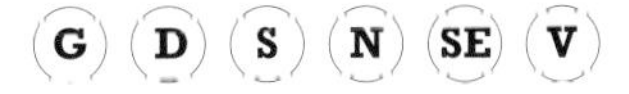

Nutritional information per serving
Kcals 83 | **Protein** 6.3g
Carbohydrates 10.3g, of which sugars 9.7g
Fat 1.2g, of which saturates 0.2g

Skin Refresher

¼ small cantaloupe melon, skin cut off
1 handful of seedless red grapes
2 celery sticks
1 courgette
¼ cucumber
1 lime, peeled
4 mint sprigs
2 drops of MILK THISTLE tincture (optional)
½ tsp BAOBAB powder

Take this wonderfully cleansing juice for its skin-beautifying and hydrating properties. Milk thistle supports the liver, whereas melon provides potassium to balance the body's fluids, helping to relieve bloating and water retention.

Put all the ingredients, except the milk thistle and baobab, through an electric juicer. Stir in the milk thistle and baobab, and serve immediately.

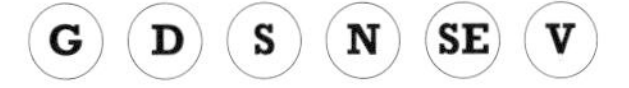

Nutritional information per serving
Kcals 83 | **Protein** 4.1g
Carbohydrates 13.8g, of which sugars 13.6g
Fat 0.9g, of which saturates 0.1g

1 large handful of fresh or frozen blueberries
1 green apple
½ cucumber
1 romaine lettuce
1 tsp SUPERBERRY powder
½ tsp SPIRULINA powder

Turn back the clock and protect your body from damage by harmful free-radicals with this antioxidant-rich juice. It contains phytochemicals, including anthocyanidins and resveratrol, which have been shown to be potent anti-ageing compounds. Spirulina cleanses the body as well as adding protein to the juice.

Put all the ingredients, except the superberry and spirulina, through an electric juicer. Stir in the superberry and spirulina, and serve immediately.

Nutritional information per serving
Kcals 119 | **Protein** 5.9g
Carbohydrates 18.6g, of which sugars 17.5g
Fat 2.1g, of which saturates 0.3g

Pictured>

2 green apples
1 lemon, peeled
4 celery sticks
½ cucumber
1 handful of coriander leaves
2 drops of ZEOLITE liquid (optional)
¼ tsp CHLORELLA powder

Take this purifying apple and celery juice to cleanse the body, fight infection and detoxify heavy metals. It's ideal to initiate a healthier-eating programme, boost energy levels and improve skin health. Zeolite is an effective chelator of toxins, whereas chlorella supports cleansing and energy levels.

Put all the ingredients, except the zeolite, if using, and the chlorella, through an electric juicer. Stir in the zeolite and chlorella, and serve immediately.

Nutritional information per serving
Kcals 93 | **Protein** 3.3g
Carbohydrates 18.1g, of which sugars 18.1g
Fat 0.7g, of which saturates 0g

Morning Zest

1 pink grapefruit, peeled
1 lemon, peeled
1cm/½in piece of root ginger
1 large handful of cos or romaine lettuce leaves
¼ tsp SHILAJIT powder
½ tsp MACA powder
½ tsp GINKGO powder
a pinch of stevia or xylitol, to taste (optional)

This citrus burst will fuel your brain and help to increase your focus and concentration throughout the day. The combination of the herbs shilajit, maca and gingko nourishes your cells, increases stamina and enhances energy production. It's a great pick-me-up juice to take at any time of the day.

Put all the ingredients, except the powders and stevia, through an electric juicer. Transfer to a blender or food processor and add the powders, then blend to combine. Sweeten with stevia, if needed. Stir and serve immediately.

Health Benefits

Shilajit is one of the top supplements in Ayurvedic medicine and is made from a brown pitch that exudes from the layers of rocks. It supplies a wealth of dietary minerals and trace minerals along with fulvic acid to help detoxify the body. Gingko is an excellent brain tonic, rich in antioxidants. It may help to improve cognitive function, because it promotes good blood circulation in the brain and protects it from neuronal damage.

G D S N SE V

Nutritional information per serving
Kcals 66 | **Protein** 2.3g
Carbohydrates 12.7g, of which sugars 11.7g
Fat 0.5g, of which saturates 0.1g

½ sweet potato, cut into cubes
1 handful of winter greens, such as Swiss chard or kale, chopped
2 tsp maple syrup, YACON syrup or coconut syrup
2 tbsp pecan nuts
¼ tsp vanilla extract
½ tsp ground cinnamon
a pinch of freshly grated nutmeg
1 tbsp LUCUMA powder
2 pitted soft dried dates, chopped
1 tsp chopped pecan nuts

Drink this spicy smoothie instead of lunch or for a breakfast on the go.

Cook the sweet potato in a pan of boiling water for 10–15 minutes until tender. Drain in a colander and leave to cool. Put the sweet potato into a blender or food processor and add the remaining ingredients, except the chopped pecans. Add 250ml/9fl oz/1 cup water and blend until smooth and creamy. Serve with the chopped pecans scattered over the top.

Nutritional information per serving
Kcals 441 | **Protein** 6.1g
Carbohydrates 45.4g, of which sugars 18.8g
Fat 25.6g, of which saturates 2.2g

30g/1oz/scant ¼ cup HEMP PROTEIN powder
1 tsp CHIA SEEDS
1 large handful of spinach leaves, chopped
½ lime, peeled
¼ small pineapple, skin cut off, chopped
250ml/9fl oz/1 cup GREEN TEA, cooled, or ¼ tsp MATCHA GREEN TEA powder mixed with 250ml/9fl oz/1 cup water
½ tsp WHEATGRASS powder

Kick-start your day with this protein-packed juice. The green-tea base helps boost fat burning and metabolism, whereas the protein powder will support blood sugar balance and keep you energized all morning. For an exceptionally potent kick, use matcha green tea powder.

Put all the ingredients into a blender or food processor and blend until smooth and creamy. Serve immediately.

Nutritional information per serving
Kcals 226 | **Protein** 18.9g
Carbohydrates 24.4g, of which sugars 15.7g
Fat 5.9g, of which saturates 0.2g

1 large handful of kale leaves, chopped
250ml/9fl oz/1 cup KOMBUCHA (page 21)
¼ small pineapple, skin cut off, chopped
1 handful of mint leaves
½ lime, peeled
5 ice cubes
¼ tsp WHEATGRASS powder

Hydrating and probiotic-rich, this fruity kale drink, with a base of kombucha, is an ideal smoothie to support your immune health and digestive system while dieting or as part of a maintenance programme. The wheatgrass enhances the cleansing process to promote healthy weight loss.

Put all the ingredients into a blender or food processor and blend until smooth and creamy. Serve immediately.

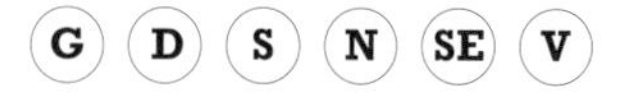

Nutritional information per serving
Kcals 100 | **Protein** 0.9g
Carbohydrates 22.3g, of which sugars 14.5g
Fat 0.4g, of which saturates 0g

60g/2¼oz canned pumpkin purée, or cooked pumpkin or butternut squash, puréed
1 handful of spinach leaves, chopped
½ banana, peeled and chopped
½ tsp ground cinnamon
½ tsp vanilla extract
250ml/9fl oz/1 cup almond milk
1 tsp COCONUT OIL
1 tsp almond nut butter
½ tsp CAMU CAMU powder
1 tsp MANUKA or RAW HONEY, or YACON syrup

Coconut oil is added to this pumpkin smoothie to enhance its creamy and satisfying taste. It can also boost energy quickly. Camu camu berry will give you an extra shot of immune-boosting vitamin C too.

Put all the ingredients into a blender or food processor and blend until smooth and creamy. Serve immediately.

Nutritional information per serving
Kcals 215 | **Protein** 4.8g
Carbohydrates 52.6g, of which sugars 12.5g
Fat 8.5g, of which saturates 3.2g

1 banana, peeled
1 tbsp almond nut butter
1 handful of kale or spinach leaves, chopped
½ tsp ground cinnamon
1 tbsp RAW CACAO powder
½ tsp MACA powder
¼ tsp ASHWAGANDHA powder
a pinch of stevia or xylitol, to taste (optional)
4 ice cubes

This creamy shake mineralizes the body, increases focus, energy and libido, and relieves stress.

Chop the banana and put it into a freezer bag. Exclude all the air, then seal and freeze overnight or until solid. Put the banana into a blender or food processor and add the remaining ingredients, except the stevia and ice. Add 250ml/9fl oz/1 cup water and blend until smooth. Sweeten with stevia, if needed. Add the ice and blend to create a slushy drink.

Nutritional information per serving
Kcals 262 | **Protein** 7.9g
Carbohydrates 35.4g, of which sugars 21g
Fat 9.6g, of which saturates 2.4g

1 ripe pear, cored and chopped
2 tbsp cashew nuts
1 handful of cos or romaine lettuce leaves, chopped
250ml/9fl oz/1 cup almond milk
1 tbsp lime juice
1 tsp CHIA SEEDS
a pinch of stevia or xylitol, to taste (optional)

Chia seeds add plenty of soluble fibre to this nutty smoothie, to support digestive health and keep your blood sugar level stable. This will mean fewer energy dips and cravings, making it easier to control weight. Cashew nuts contain protein and healthy fats. All in all, it's a good grab-and-go breakfast.

Put all the ingredients, except the stevia, into a blender or food processor and blend until smooth and creamy. Sweeten with stevia, if needed. Stir and serve immediately.

Nutritional information per serving
Kcals 296 | **Protein** 7.4g
Carbohydrates 24.6g, of which sugars 9.3g
Fat 18.7g, of which saturates 3g

Wheatgrass Ginger Cooler

1 handful of romaine lettuce leaves, chopped
½ tsp WHEATGRASS powder or GREEN SUPERFOOD blend
a thin slice of peeled root ginger
1 ripe pear, cored and chopped
1 celery stick, chopped
¼ avocado, peeled and chopped
1 handful of ice cubes

Avocado and pear make a silky base for this smoothie, which is perfect for reducing fatigue and improving digestion while on a weight-loss or weight-maintenance plan. Wheatgrass is added for its super-rich supply of minerals, essential enzymes and amino acids, plus chlorophyll to boost a detox.

Put all the ingredients, except the ice, into a blender or food processor. Add 250ml/9fl oz/1 cup water and blend until smooth and creamy. Add the ice and blend to create a slushy drink. Serve immediately.

G D S N SE CI V

Nutritional information per serving
Kcals 89 | **Protein** 1.4g
Carbohydrates 8.4g, of which sugars 7.7g
Fat 5.2g, of which saturates 1.1g

Creamy Infection Fighter

1 small banana, peeled
1 handful of fresh or frozen cranberries
1 handful of coriander leaves
1 handful of cos or romaine lettuce, chopped
½ tsp BAOBAB powder
250ml/9fl oz/1 cup WATER KEFIR (page 20) or KOMBUCHA (page 21)

This light, purifying drink is perfect for digestive health and for reducing bloating too. Keep some cranberries in the freezer to make this tart, infection-busting smoothie. Cranberries are rich in proanthocyanidins, which have been shown to prevent cystitis and urinary tract infections.

Chop the banana and put it into a freezer bag. Exclude all the air, then seal and freeze overnight or until solid. Put the banana into a blender or food processor and add the remaining ingredients. Blend until smooth and creamy. Serve immediately.

Nutritional information per serving
Kcals 142 | **Protein** 1.8g
Carbohydrates 31.7g, of which sugars 21.7g
Fat 0.5g, of which saturates 0.1g

Workout Recovery

30g/1oz/scant ¼ cup VANILLA PROTEIN powder
1 banana, peeled
1 handful of kale leaves, chopped
250ml/9fl oz/1 cup coconut water
1 tsp GOJI BERRY powder
½ tsp MACA powder
1 tsp ROYAL JELLY powder or BEE POLLEN

Pack this smoothie in your gym bag to take after you have finished a workout. It is abundant in electrolytes, to quickly hydrate your body, and protein to optimize muscle recovery and repair. It also contains maca to support adrenal health and improve blood sugar balance, making it easier for you to lose weight.

Put all the ingredients into a blender or food processor and blend until smooth and creamy. Serve immediately or store as described on page 10 to drink later.

Health Benefits

The combination of maca and royal jelly nourishes the body, especially the adrenal glands after intense exercise. Kale is a great source of magnesium, which is lost via sweat during a workout, and this, together with low levels of potassium, can lead to muscle cramps and low energy. To speed up your recovery and lower inflammation, include a high-antioxidant berry powder like the goji berry powder used here.

G D S N SE CI

Nutritional information per serving
Kcals 299 | **Protein** 21g
Carbohydrates 42.5g, of which sugars 21.2g
Fat 5.1g, of which saturates 0.3g

Get Your Sprouts

4 Brussels sprouts
1 handful of leafy greens, chopped
¼ small pineapple, skin cut off
½ avocado, peeled and chopped
1 tbsp lime juice
250ml/9fl oz/1 cup WATER KEFIR (page 20) or KOMBUCHA (page 21)
2 tbsp INCAN berries

Brussels sprouts are rich in many valuable nutrients, but they're frequently not the top choice as a vegetable. The answer? Drink them with avocado and pineapple. They are an excellent source of vitamins and minerals, and the combination of healthy fats and fibre makes this a satisfying drink.

Put the Brussels sprouts in a steamer over boiling water and cook for 5 minutes or until crisp-tender. Refresh under cold water. Put the Brussels sprouts into a blender or food processor and add the remaining ingredients. Blend until smooth and creamy. Serve immediately.

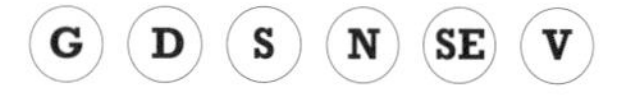

Nutritional information per serving
Kcals 242 | **Protein** 4.5g
Carbohydrates 41.5g, of which sugars 24.8g
Fat 5.6g, of which saturates 1.1g

Pictured>

1 handful of seedless red grapes
1 tbsp no-added-salt peanut butter
1 handful of spinach leaves, chopped
1 tsp CHIA SEEDS
1 tsp SUPERBERRY powder
1 tsp shelled HEMP SEEDS
250ml/9fl oz/1 cup almond milk
½ tsp vanilla extract

Intensify your workout recovery with this protein-packed smoothie, or take it as a quick-and-easy breakfast option. The recovery potential of this protective drink is enhanced by adding a spoonful of antioxidant-rich berry powder.

Put the grapes into a freezer bag. Exclude all the air, then seal and freeze overnight or until solid. Put the grapes into a blender or food processor and add the remaining ingredients. Blend until smooth and creamy. Serve immediately.

Nutritional information per serving
Kcals 272 | **Protein** 8.4g
Carbohydrates 27.5g, of which sugars 12.7g
Fat 14.6g, of which saturates 1.8g

Sweet Pea Smoothie

1 handful of frozen peas
1 handful of spinach leaves, chopped
1 tsp ground FLAXSEED
1 large handful of strawberries, hulled
250ml/9fl oz/1 cup WATER KEFIR (page 20), or coconut water plus ½ tsp PROBIOTIC powder

Frozen peas create a good, creamy texture to this hydrating blend as well as adding fibre. Use water kefir for a probiotic burst to enhance your digestive health – and take this as part of any supercharged programme.

Put all the ingredients into a blender or food processor and blend until smooth and creamy. Serve immediately.

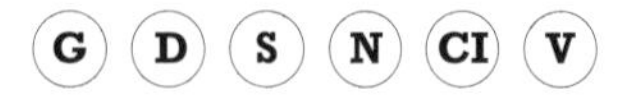

Nutritional information per serving
Kcals 97 | **Protein** 3.8g
Carbohydrates 15.1g, of which sugars 4.7g
Fat 2.3g, of which saturates 0.3g

Minted Green Tea

½ banana, peeled
4 mint leaves
¼ tsp MATCHA GREEN TEA powder
½ cucumber, chopped
1 kiwi fruit, peeled and chopped
250ml/9fl oz/1 cup water or coconut water
4 ice cubes

Cucumber is partnered with mint for this cooling summer smoothie. It's low in calories and full of fat-burning matcha tea, so it's a great way to fire up your metabolism. As well as being hydrating, cucumber is a source of silica, which can help fight wrinkles.

Chop the banana and put it into a freezer bag. Exclude all the air, then seal and freeze overnight or until solid. Put the banana into a blender or food processor and add the remaining ingredients, except the ice. Blend until smooth. Add the ice and blend until smooth and icy.

Nutritional information per serving
Kcals 94 | **Protein** 4.6g
Carbohydrates 17.4g, of which sugars 16.5g
Fat 0.6g, of which saturates 0g

Cauliflower Caramel

½ banana, peeled
4 cauliflower florets
1 tsp cashew nut butter
1 handful of lettuce leaves, chopped
3 large pitted soft dried dates, chopped
1 tbsp LUCUMA powder
¼ tsp ground cinnamon
½ tsp vanilla extract
1 tsp YACON syrup
250ml/9fl oz/1 cup coconut milk

Crammed with vitamins and minerals, this sweet and creamy blend will energize your body. Yacon syrup and lucuma powder give the drink a healthy caramel-like flavour without upsetting blood sugar levels.

Chop the banana and put it into a freezer bag. Exclude all the air, then seal and freeze overnight or until solid. Put the cauliflower in a steamer over boiling water and cook for 8 minutes or until crisp-tender. Refresh under cold water.

Put the banana into a blender or food processor and add the cauliflower and the remaining ingredients. Blend until smooth and creamy. Serve immediately.

G D S SE CI V

Nutritional information per serving
Kcals 252 | **Protein** 5.2g
Carbohydrates 51.5g, of which sugars 37.1g
Fat 4g, of which saturates 1.2g

Brain Invigorator

1 tbsp RAW CACAO powder
1 handful of spinach leaves, chopped
1 tbsp LUCUMA powder
1 tsp SUNFLOWER LECITHIN GRANULES
1 tsp MCT OIL or COCONUT OIL
2 heaped tbsp macadamia nuts
1 tsp MANUKA or RAW HONEY
½ tsp MACA powder
250ml/9fl oz/1 cup GYNOSTEMMA TEA or GREEN TEA

For a mental boost while on your weight-maintenance or weight-loss programme, try this natural pick-me-up to nourish your mind – and your body. By including protein and healthy fats you help to stabilize blood sugar levels and create a very satisfying, filling drink – perfect as a breakfast option that will keep you energized through the morning until lunchtime.

Put all the ingredients into a blender or food processor and blend until smooth and creamy. Serve immediately.

Health Benefits

Gynostemma has invigorating and adaptogenic properties. It is anti-ageing, anti-inflammatory, antioxidant and super-calming. Gynostemma can be helpful for reducing stress and improving focus and concentration, which may help to make it easier for you to stick to your healthy-eating plan. It's also a great herb for improving and strengthening your digestion.

G D S CI

Nutritional information per serving
Kcals 412 | **Protein** 7.3g
Carbohydrates 28.4g, of which sugars 6.5g
Fat 27.8g, of which saturates 6.7g

½ tsp **GREEN COFFEE** powder
125ml/4fl oz/½ cup almond milk
1 small handful of spinach leaves, chopped
2 tbsp **RAW CACAO** powder
3 large pitted medjool dates, chopped
½ tsp vanilla extract
6 ice cubes

Try green coffee powder to give you that natural lift in the morning. It is also useful for promoting weight loss, because its chemical compounds – caffeine and chlorogenic acid – help to break down stored fats. This mix is also a great way to boost your metabolism.

Put all the ingredients, except the ice, into a blender or food processor and add 250ml/9fl oz/1 cup hot water. Blend until smooth and creamy. Add the ice and blend until smooth. Serve immediately.

Nutritional information per serving
Kcals 199 | **Protein** 6.5g
Carbohydrates 33.8g, of which sugars 10g
Fat 3.9g, of which saturates 1.5g

Pictured>

⅛ cantaloupe melon, skin cut off, chopped
1 tsp **CHIA SEEDS**
1 tbsp lime juice
1 tbsp **GOJI BERRIES**
1 handful of parsley
1 handful of cos or romaine lettuce leaves, chopped
200ml/7fl oz/scant 1 cup natural probiotic yogurt or **MILK KEFIR** (page 20)
150ml/5fl oz/scant ⅔ cup orange juice

Get up and go with this fruity summer blend. Protein-rich probiotic yogurt or milk kefir gives it a wonderful creamy texture as well as benefitting the digestion and providing energy. The smoothie is also high in vitamin C and antioxidants, making it a revitalizing and satisfying drink.

Put all the ingredients into a blender or food processor and blend until smooth and creamy. Serve immediately.

Nutritional information per serving
Kcals 280 | **Protein** 12.7g
Carbohydrates 46.7g, of which sugars 43.6g
Fat 4.9g, of which saturates 1.5g

½ mango, peeled and chopped
250ml/9fl oz/1 cup COCONUT KEFIR (page 20)
½ lime, peeled
1 handful of spinach leaves, chopped
1 TOCOTRIENOLS capsule, squeezed, or ¼ tsp powder or 1 vitamin E capsule
½ tsp BAOBAB powder or ¼ tsp CAMU CAMU powder

Coconut kefir, as the base of this smoothie, contains essential beneficial bacteria, healthy fat and protein, helping to stabilize blood sugar and optimize weight loss. Packed with vitamin C, this is a wonderfully energizing and immune-supporting drink.

Put all the ingredients into a blender or food processor and blend until smooth and creamy. Serve immediately.

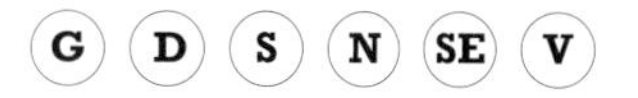

Nutritional information per serving
Kcals 199 | **Protein** 14.6g
Carbohydrates 51.3g, of which sugars 5.8g
Fat 2.5g, of which saturates 0.1g

1 handful of red cabbage leaves, chopped
1 tbsp dried cherries or INCAN BERRIES
1 tbsp GOJI BERRIES
½ tsp ACAI BERRY powder
1 tsp COCONUT OIL
1 handful of fresh or frozen blueberries
1 handful of pitted frozen cherries
1 handful of spinach leaves, chopped

Here is a meal in a glass containing health-giving cabbage, a cruciferous vegetable containing glucosinolates, which support detoxification, particularly of oestrogen. Adding berries makes it deliciously sweet. The coconut oil is an energizing fat to keep you feeling great.

Put all the ingredients into a blender or food processor and add 250ml/9fl oz/1 cup water. Blend until smooth and creamy. Serve the smoothie immediately.

Nutritional information per serving
Kcals 171 | **Protein** 2.5g
Carbohydrates 31.1g, of which sugars 28.4g
Fat 4.3g, of which saturates 2.6g

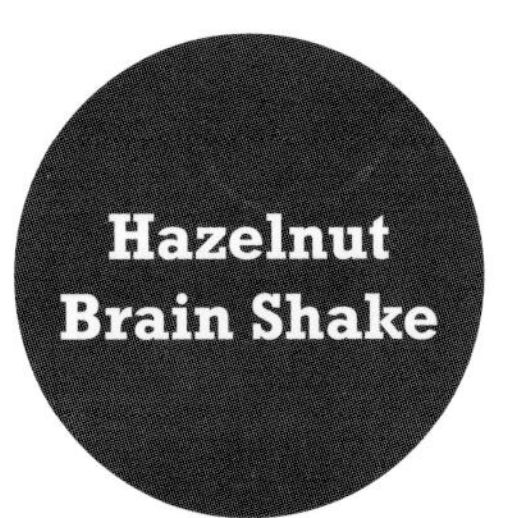

4 broccoli florets
30g/1oz/¼ cup hazelnuts
1 tbsp RAW CACAO powder
1 tbsp LUCUMA powder
¼ tsp MUCUNA PRURIENS powder
1 tsp xylitol, coconut syrup, or MANUKA or RAW HONEY
250ml/9fl oz/1 cup semi-skimmed milk, or almond milk or coconut milk

If you like chocolate spread, you'll love this chocolate blend – and you would never guess it also contains broccoli! Also added is *Mucuna pruriens*, which has long been used in Ayurvedic medicine for reducing body fat. Mucuna also promotes a sense of well-being, increases energy levels and provides L-dopa to boost mood.

Put the broccoli in a steamer over boiling water and cook for 5 minutes or until crisp-tender. Refresh under cold water. Put the hazelnuts in a dry saucepan and cook over a medium-high heat for 5 minutes or until lightly toasted, tossing frequently. Put the broccoli into a blender or food processor and add the nuts and the remaining ingredients. Blend until smooth and creamy. Serve immediately.

(G) (S) (SE) (CI)

Nutritional information per serving
Kcals 452 | **Protein** 17.3g
Carbohydrates 41.1g, of which sugars 15.2g
Fat 24.6g, of which saturates 4.9g

Golden Vanilla Milk

1 handful of cos or romaine lettuce leaves, chopped
40g/1½oz/¼ cup almonds, soaked overnight in water and drained
1 tbsp coconut flakes
1 tsp MANUKA or RAW HONEY, or YACON syrup
1 tsp BEE POLLEN
¼ tsp ground TURMERIC
¼ tsp ground cinnamon
a pinch of cardamom
1 vanilla pod or ½ tsp vanilla extract or powder

Almonds blended with turmeric and warming spices make this a health-supporting, anti-inflammatory and mineral-rich smoothie. It's a comforting shake and ideal for balancing blood sugar, making it effective for weight control. To improve digestion, soak the almonds in water overnight, then drain and rinse them before using.

Put all the ingredients, except the vanilla, into a blender or food processor. If using a vanilla pod, cut the pod in half and scrape the seeds into the blender (save the pod for another use), or add the extract. Add 250ml/9fl oz/1 cup water and blend until smooth and creamy. Serve the smoothie immediately.

Health Benefits
Turmeric is one of the best anti-inflammatory spices – rich in curcumin, the active constituent shown to be beneficial for numerous inflammatory health conditions and supporting cognitive function. Inflammation is also associated with weight gain and changes in insulin function, so adding turmeric is a great way to improve weight loss or as part of a maintenance diet. The addition of bee pollen provides a wealth of amino acids, enzymes and antioxidants to support health and vitality.

G D S SE CI

Nutritional information per serving
Kcals 337 | **Protein** 10.5g
Carbohydrates 9g, of which sugars 6.3g

The Quick Look

(W) **Weight loss (fat-burner)** The drinks are graded as: 5 stars (200 calories or less) – best for weight loss; 4 stars (201–250 calories); 3 stars (251–300 calories); 2 stars (301–350 calories); 1 star (351–400 calories).

(C) **Cleansing (encompassing detoxing and digestion)** To help support the detoxification system and the removal of toxins. They are also soothing for the digestive system.

(R) **Radiance (anti-ageing)** Containing known 'beauty nutrients' to promote youthful, glowing skin, nails and hair as well as possessing anti-ageing properties.

(E) **Energy** To boost performance and energy levels, for balancing blood sugar and with nutrients for sustained energy and to enhance muscle mass.

(I) **Immune boost** To support the body's immune system. The drinks may also contain ingredients that have anti-microbial and anti-viral properties.

(B) **Brain health and stress** For brain and cognitive health, including vitamins, minerals, healthy fats and antioxidants essential for optimal brain function.

Deep Green (page 28)

W ★★★★★
C ★★★★★
R ★★★
E ★★★
I ★
B ★

Parsley Perfection (page 28)

W ★★★★★
C ★★★★★
R ★★★
E ★★★
I ★
B ★

Green Purity (page 30)

W ★★★★★
C ★★★★★
R ★★★★
E ★★★
I ★★
B ★

Enzyme Support (page 32)

W ★★★★★
C ★★★★★
R ★★★
E ★★
I ★
B ★

Liver Flush (page 32)

W ★★★★★
C ★★★★★
R ★★
E ★★
I ★
B ★

Minted Kale (page 34)

W ★★★★★
C ★★★★
R ★★
E ★★
I ★
B ★

Light and Fresh (page 34)

W ★★★★★
C ★★★★
R ★★
E ★★★
I ★★
B ★

Immune Blast (page 35)

W ★★★★
C ★★
R ★★★
E ★★
I ★★★★★
B ★★

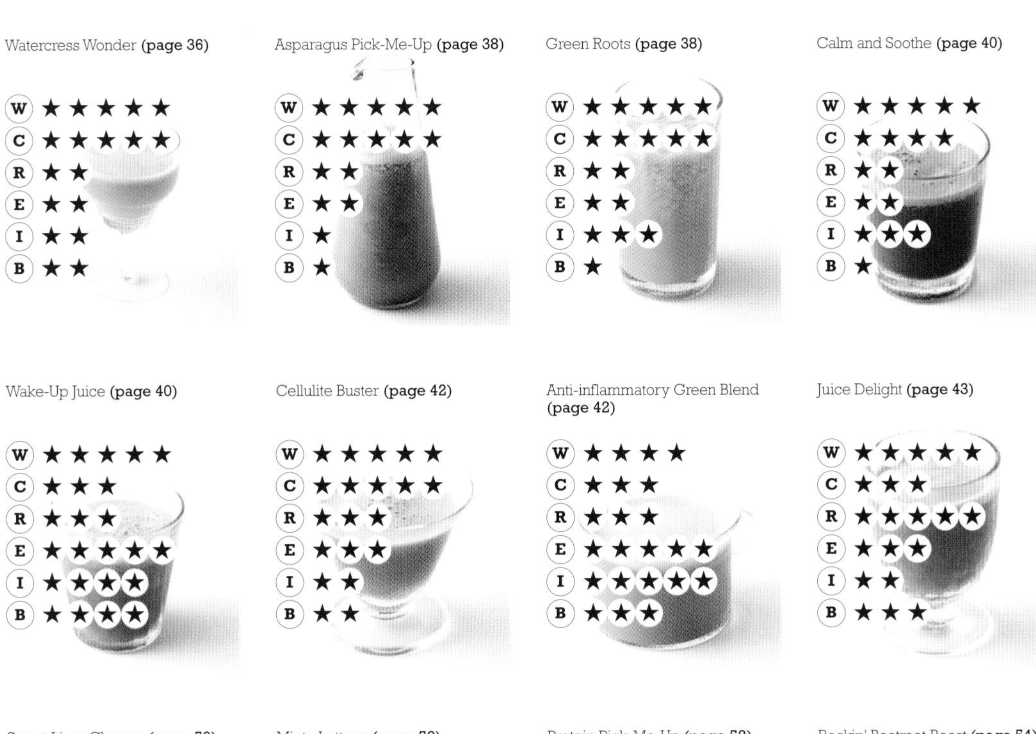

Watercress Wonder **(page 36)**

W ★★★★★
C ★★★★★
R ★★
E ★★
I ★★
B ★★

Asparagus Pick-Me-Up **(page 38)**

W ★★★★★
C ★★★★★
R ★★
E ★★
I ★
B ★

Green Roots **(page 38)**

W ★★★★★
C ★★★★★
R ★★
E ★★
I ★★★
B ★

Calm and Soothe **(page 40)**

W ★★★★★
C ★★★★
R ★★
E ★★
I ★★★
B ★

Wake-Up Juice **(page 40)**

W ★★★★★
C ★★★
R ★★★
E ★★★★★
I ★★★★
B ★★★★

Cellulite Buster **(page 42)**

W ★★★★★
C ★★★★★
R ★★★
E ★★★
I ★★
B ★★

Anti-inflammatory Green Blend **(page 42)**

W ★★★★
C ★★★
R ★★★
E ★★★★★
I ★★★★★
B ★★★

Juice Delight **(page 43)**

W ★★★★★
C ★★★
R ★★★★★
E ★★★
I ★★
B ★★★

Sweet Liver Cleanse **(page 50)**

W ★★★★
C ★★★
R ★★★★
E ★★★
I ★★
B ★

Minty Lettuce **(page 50)**

W ★★★★★
C ★★★
R ★★★
E ★★★★
I ★★★
B ★★

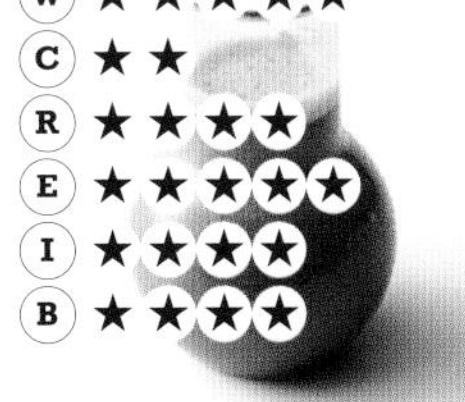

Protein Pick-Me-Up **(page 52)**

W ★★★★★
C ★★
R ★★★★
E ★★★★★
I ★★★★
B ★★★★

Rockin' Beetroot Boost **(page 54)**

W ★★★★★
C ★★★★★
R ★★★★
E ★★★
I ★★
B ★★

Gut Healer **(page 54)**

W ★★★★★
C ★★★
R ★★
E ★★★
I ★★★
B ★★

Red-Carpet Cleanse **(page 56)**

W ★★★★
C ★★★
R ★★★★★
E ★★★★
I ★★★
B ★★★

Kale Supreme **(page 56)**

W ★★★★★
C ★★★★
R ★★★
E ★★★★
I ★★★
B ★★

Longevity Nectar **(page 57)**

W ★★★★★
C ★★★★★
R ★★★
E ★★★
I ★★★
B ★★★

Spring Freshen-Up **(page 58)**

W ★★★★★
C ★★★★★
R ★★★
E ★★★
I ★★
B ★

Protein Boost **(page 58)**

W ★★★★★
C ★★★★★
R ★★★
E ★★★
I ★★
B ★★

Hormone Cleanse **(page 60)**

W ★★★★★
C ★★★★★
R ★★★★★
E ★★★
I ★★
B ★★

Skin Nourish **(page 62)**

W ★★★★★
C ★★★
R ★★★★
E ★★★
I ★★
B ★★

Power Immune Greens **(page 62)**

W ★★★★★
C ★★★★
R ★★★
E ★★
I ★★★★
B ★★

Easy Greens **(page 64)**

W ★★★★★
C ★★★★★
R ★★★
E ★★★
I ★★
B ★

Invigorate **(page 64)**

W ★★★★★
C ★★★
R ★★★
E ★★★
I ★★
B ★★★★

Vanilla Cashew Cream **(page 65)**

W ★★★
C ★★
R ★★★★
E ★★★★★
I ★★★
B ★★★

Muscle Booster **(page 65)**

W ★★★
C ★★
R ★★★★
E ★★★
I ★★
B ★★★

Beauty Detox **(page 66)**

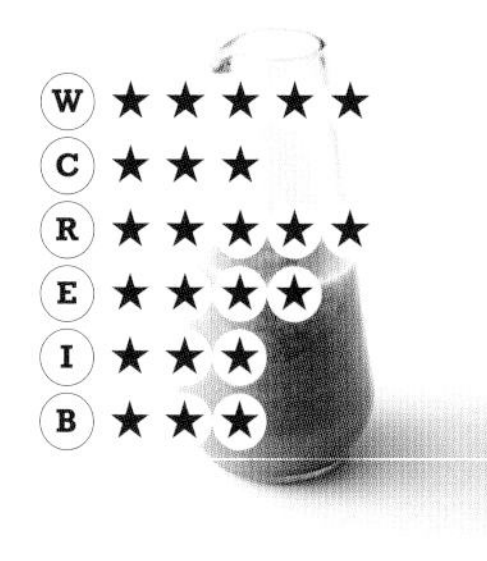

W ★★★★★
C ★★★
R ★★★★★
E ★★★★
I ★★★
B ★★★

Chocolate Fix **(page 68)**

W ★
C ★★
R ★★★★★
E ★★★★★
I ★★★
B ★★★

Matcha Fat Burner **(page 68)**

W ★★★
C ★★★
R ★★★★★
E ★★★★★
I ★★★
B ★★★

Get the Glow **(page 70)**

W ★★★
C ★★
R ★★★★★
E ★★★★
I ★★★
B ★★★

Spinach Energizer **(page 70)**

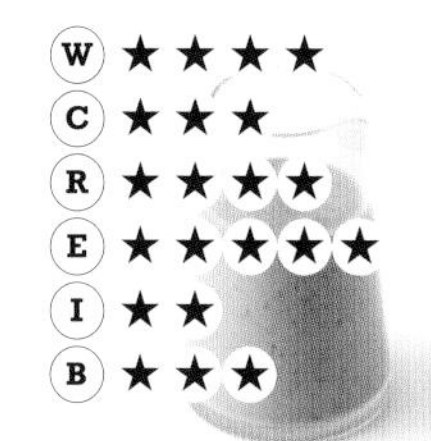

W ★★★★
C ★★★
R ★★★★
E ★★★★★
I ★★
B ★★★

Rich Green Immune Nectar **(page 78)**

W ★★★★★
C ★★★★★
R ★★★★
E ★★★
I ★★★★
B ★★

Basil Green Cream **(page 78)**

W ★★★★★
C ★★★★★
R ★★★
E ★★★
I ★★
B ★

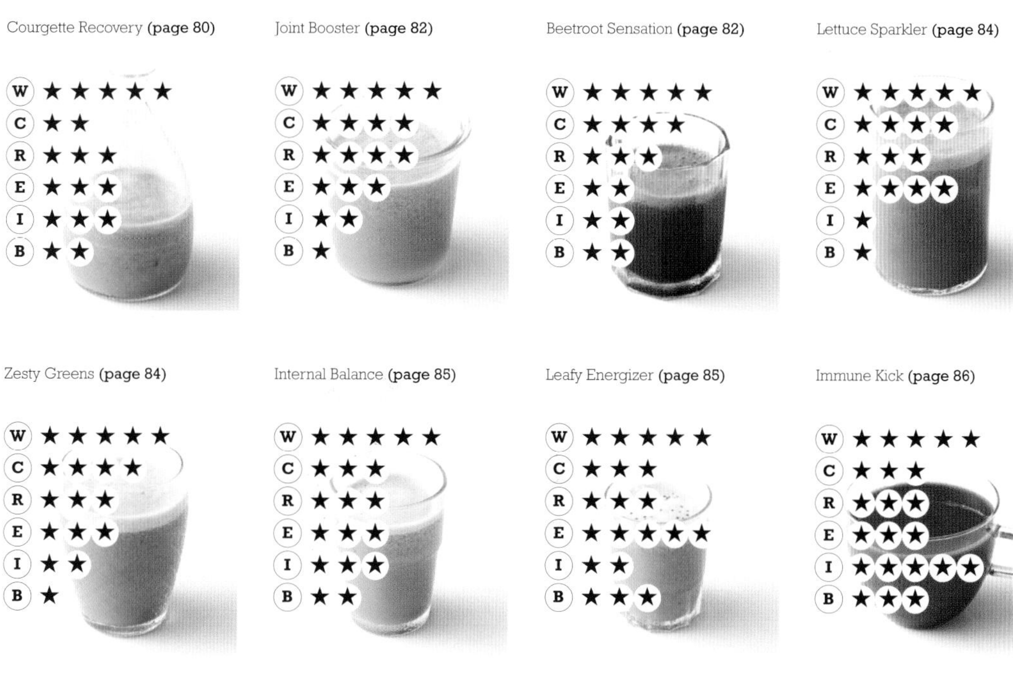

Recipe	W	C	R	E	I	B
Courgette Recovery **(page 80)**	★★★★★	★★	★★★	★★★	★★★	★★
Joint Booster **(page 82)**	★★★★★	★★★★	★★★★	★★★	★★	★
Beetroot Sensation **(page 82)**	★★★★★	★★★★	★★★	★★	★★	★★
Lettuce Sparkler **(page 84)**	★★★★★	★★★★	★★★	★★★★	★	★

Recipe	W	C	R	E	I	B
Zesty Greens **(page 84)**	★★★★★	★★★★	★★★	★★★	★★	★
Internal Balance **(page 85)**	★★★★★	★★★	★★★	★★★	★★★	★★
Leafy Energizer **(page 85)**	★★★★★	★★★	★★★	★★★★★	★★	★★★
Immune Kick **(page 86)**	★★★★★	★★★	★★★	★★★	★★★★★	★★★

Recipe	W	C	R	E	I	B
Gingerbread Shake **(page 88)**	★★★★★	★★★	★★★	★★★★★	★★★★	★★★★
Warming Detox Shake **(page 88)**	★★★★★	★★★★	★★	★★	★★	★
Chocolate Almond Recovery **(page 90)**	★	★	★★★★★	★★★★★	★★★	★★★
Iced Tea Cooler **(page 90)**	★★★★★	★★★	★★★★★	★★★	★★	★

Recipe	W	C	R	E	I	B
Bedtime Blend **(page 92)**	★★★	★★	★★★★	★★★★	★★★	★★★
Tropical Greens **(page 92)**	★★★★	★★★	★★★	★★★	★★	★★
Vitamin C Burst **(page 93)**	★★★★★	★★★★	★★★	★★★★	★★	★★
Carrot Recovery Fix **(page 94)**	★★★★	★★	★★★	★★★	★★★★	★★

Joint Support **(page 94)**

W ★★★★
C ★★
R ★★★★
E ★★★★
I ★★★
B ★★★

Warm Elixir **(page 96)**

Coconut Perfection **(page 98)**

W ★★★★★
C ★★
R ★★★
E ★★★★
I ★★
B ★★

Green Nourishment **(page 98)**

Vegan Trainer **(page 100)**

Probiotic Blast **(page 100)**

Kombucha Cleanse **(page 101)**

Green Kefir **(page 101)**

Hormone Boost **(page 102)**

Antioxidant Blast **(page 104)**

Mint Chocolate Chip **(page 104)**

Stress Buster **(page 106)**

Pre-Workout Greens **(page 108)**

Thai Cream **(page 108)**

W ★★★
C ★★
R ★★★
E ★★★
I ★★★★★
B ★★★

Longevity Boost **(page 109)**

Maca Mocha **(page 109)**

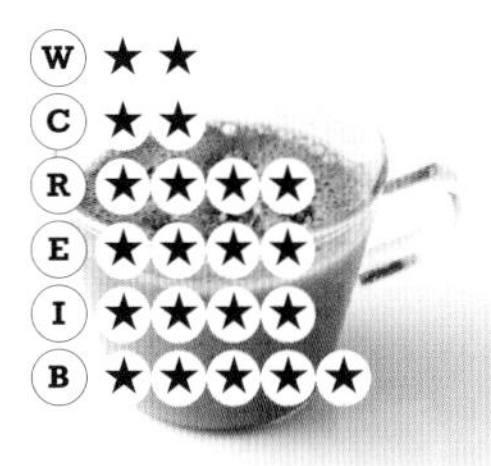

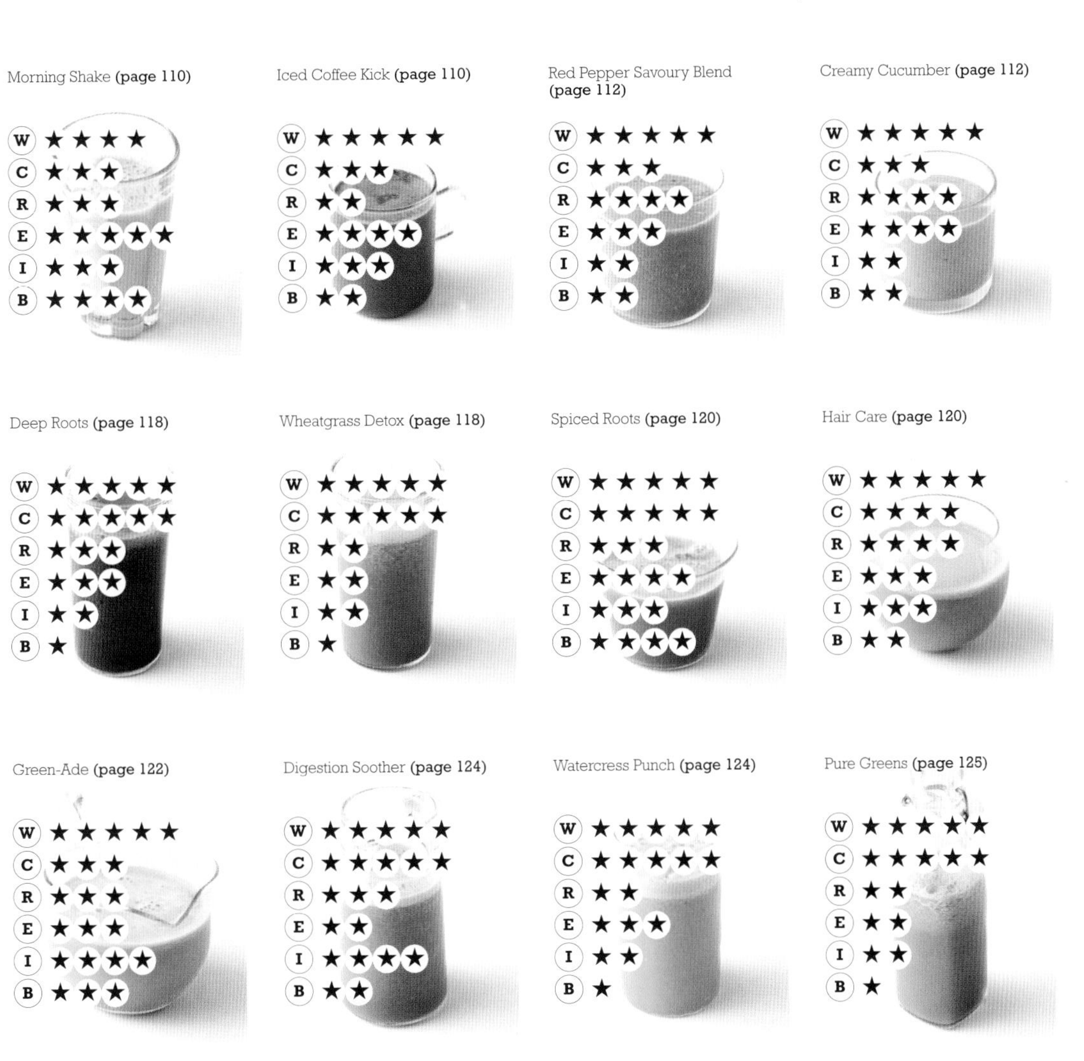

Morning Shake (page 110)

Iced Coffee Kick (page 110)

Red Pepper Savoury Blend (page 112)

Creamy Cucumber (page 112)

Deep Roots (page 118)

Wheatgrass Detox (page 118)

Spiced Roots (page 120)

Hair Care (page 120)

Green-Ade (page 122)

Digestion Soother (page 124)

Watercress Punch (page 124)

Pure Greens (page 125)

Skin Refresher (page 125)

Anti-Ageing Greens (page 126)

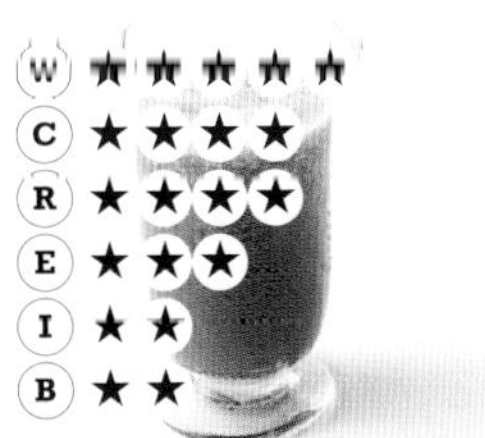

Coriander Blast (page 126)

Morning Zest (page 128)

Pecan Sweet Potato Cream **(page 130)**

W
C ★
R ★★★★
E ★★★★
I ★★★
B ★

Power Greens **(page 130)**

W ★★★★
C ★★★
R ★★★★
E ★★★★★
I ★★★
B ★★★★

Probiotic Mojito **(page 132)**

W ★★★★★
C ★★
R ★★★
E ★★★★
I ★★★★★
B ★★

Pumpkin Spice **(page 132)**

W ★★★★
C ★
R ★★★★
E ★★★★
I ★★★
B ★★

Chocolate Dream **(page 133)**

W ★★★
C ★★
R ★★★
E ★★★★
I ★★★★
B ★★★★★

Nut Greens **(page 133)**

W ★★★
C ★★
R ★★★
E ★★★
I ★★
B ★★

Wheatgrass Ginger Cooler **(page 134)**

W ★★★★★
C ★★★
R ★★★
E ★★★
I ★★
B ★★

Creamy Infection Fighter **(page 134)**

W ★★★★★
C ★★★
R ★★★
E ★★★
I ★★★★★
B ★★

Workout Recovery **(page 136)**

W ★★★
C ★★
R ★★★
E ★★★★
I ★★★★
B ★★★★

Get Your Sprouts **(page 138)**

W ★★★★
C ★★
R ★★★
E ★★★
I ★★★★
B ★★

Peanut Butter Jelly Smoothie **(page 138)**

W ★★★
C ★★
R ★★★★
E ★★★★
I ★★
B ★★

Sweet Pea Smoothie **(page 140)**

W ★★★★★
C ★★★★
R ★★★
E ★★★
I ★★
B ★★

Minted Green Tea **(page 140)**

W ★★★★★
C ★★★
R ★★★
E ★★★★
I ★★
B ★★★

Cauliflower Caramel **(page 141)**

W ★★★
C ★★
R ★★★
E ★★★
I ★★
B ★

Brain Invigorator **(page 142)**

W
C ★
R ★★★★
E ★★★★★
I ★★★★★
B ★★★★★

Green Mocha **(page 144)**

W ★★★★★
C ★★★
R ★★★
E ★★★★★
I ★★★
B ★★★

Summer Blend **(page 144)**

Probiotic Kefir Burst **(page 146)**

Cabbage Salad **(page 146)**

Hazelnut Brain Shake **(page 147)**

Golden Vanilla Milk **(page 148)**

Index

NOURISH
EAT WELL, LIVE WELL